Exclusive distributors:
Music Sales Limited
8/9 Frith Street, London W1D 3JB, England.
Music Sales Pty Limited
120 Rothschild Avenue, Rosebery, NSW 2018, Australia.

Order No. AM971597 ISBN 0-7119-8997-4
This book © Copyright 2001 by Wise Publications.

Ringtones arranged by Lucy Holliday.
Cover and book design by Phil Gambrill.
Photographs courtesy of London Features International.
Printed in Malta by Interprint Ltd.

Music Sales' complete catalogue describes thousands of
titles and is available in full colour sections by subject, direct from
Music Sales Limited. Please state your areas of interest and send
a cheque/postal order for £1.50 for postage to: Music Sales Limited,
Newmarket Road, Bury St. Edmunds, Suffolk IP33 3YB.

www.musicsales.com

WISE PUBLICATIONS
London / New York / Sydney / Paris / Copenhagen / Madrid / Tokyo

ROCK & POP CLASSICS

JAZZ & CLASSICAL

**THIS BOOK CONTAINS OVER 200
GREAT TUNES FOR YOU TO PROGRAM
INTO YOUR MOBILE PHONE.**

Just follow these four simple steps to
customise your mobile:

1 Check that your phone has a **COMPOSER** or
RECORD MELODY function (refer to the list of
makes and model numbers on pages 6-13) and
locate this function on your phone.

2 Refer to pages 6 - 13 to find **INSTRUCTIONS**
on how to program ringtones into your phone.
Check your instruction manual for further
details on the individual operation of phones.

3 Choose the **TUNE** that you want to program
from one of the four sections in this book.

4 GET RINGING!

NOTE: You will get the best results from this
book if you have a Nokia mobile phone.
Samsung, Siemens and Ericsson models have
composer features but, due to differences in
the options available on those phones, some
melodies will work better than others.

Choose your own ringtone!
E-mail us your ringtone suggestions on
ringtones@musicsales.co.uk

SIEMENS S25

There are four pieces of information for every note in every tune in this book.

1. Note — **2.** Sharp

A#2
16

4. Duration — **3.** Octave

1. Each **NOTE** name corresponds to one of the number keys on your phone (– indicates a **REST**):

1	2	3	4	5	6	7	*
C	D	E	F	G	A	B (H)	REST

Key pad equivalent:

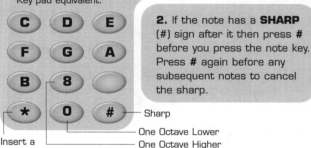

2. If the note has a **SHARP** (#) sign after it then press # before you press the note key. Press # again before any subsequent notes to cancel the sharp.

— Sharp

— One Octave Higher

— One Octave Lower

Insert a Rest

3. OCTAVE:
Use keys **8** & **0** to change the octave of the note. Choose the octave before you press the note key.

4. DURATION: Cycle through the available tone lengths with the left side key. This phone does not support 32 notes, dotted notes or different durations for rests.

TEMPO: This phone does not support tempo changes.

There are four pieces of information for every note in every tune in this book.

1. Note   **2.** Sharp

A#2
16

4. Duration   **3.** Octave

1. Each **NOTE** name corresponds to one of the number keys on your phone (– indicates a **REST**):

1	2	3	4	5	6	7	*
C	D	E	F	G	A	B (H)	REST

Key pad equivalent:

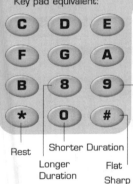

2. If the note has a **SHARP** (#) sign after it then press **9** before you press the note key. Press **9** again before any subsequent notes to cancel the sharp.

Rest — Shorter Duration — Longer Duration — Flat Sharp

3. Change **OCTAVE** using the keys on the left side of the phone - UPPER KEY: higher, LOWER key: lower. Choose the octave before you press the note key.

4. DURATION: Use keys 8 and 0 to increase and decrease the duration respectively. This phone does not support 32 notes, dotted notes or different durations for rests.

TEMPO: This phone does not support tempo changes

TIP: Tunes with fewer dotted notes and rests will sound better on this phone.

SIEMENS c35

There are four pieces of information for every note in every tune in this book.

1. Note — **2.** Sharp
4. Duration — **3.** Octave

A#2
16

1. Each **NOTE** name corresponds to one of the number keys on your phone (– indicates a **REST**):

1	2	3	4	5	6	7	0
C	D	E	F	G	A	B (H)	REST

Key pad equivalent:

(C) (D) (E)
(F) (G) (A)
(B) (C) ( )
(*) (0) (#)

2. If the note has a **SHARP** (#) sign after it then press # before you press the note key. Press # again before any subsequent notes to cancel the sharp.

— Sharp
— Insert A Rest

Change Octave

3. OCTAVE: Use the ★ key to change the octave of the note. Choose the octave before you press the note key.

4. DURATION: Hold down the note key to cycle through the available tone lengths. This phone does not support 32 notes, dotted notes or different durations for rests.

TEMPO: This phone does not support tempo changes.

TIP: This phone holds a maximum of 49 notes.

There are four pieces of information for every note in every tune in this book.

1. Note — A#2 **2.** Sharp

4. Duration — **16** **3.** Octave

1. Each **NOTE** name corresponds to one of the number keys on your phone (– indicates a **REST**):

1	2	3	4	5	6	7
C	**D**	**E**	**F**	**G**	**A**	**B (H)**

Key pad equivalent:

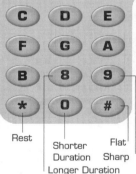

C D E
F G A
B 8 9
* 0 #

Rest — *
Shorter Duration — 8
Longer Duration — 0
Flat — #
Sharp

2. If the note has a **SHARP** (#) sign after it then press **9** before you press the note key. Press # again before any subsequent notes to cancel the sharp.

3. OCTAVE: Use the keys to change the octave of the note.

4. DURATION: Use the 8 key to make the note longer. Use the 0 key to make the note shorter. This phone does not support 32 notes, dotted notes or different durations for rests.

TEMPO: This phone does not support tempo changes

SAMSUNG A110

There are four pieces of information for every note in every tune in this book.

1. Note

2. Sharp

4. Duration

A#2
16

3. Octave

All information is entered via the **NAVIGATOR** button. To start composing a melody press the **Edit** soft key. Press the **Next** soft key to add a note.

Use the up and down arrows to make the note higher or lower.

Make note **HIGHER** (**SHARPEN**)

DURATION OF NOTE: hold to alter note lengths.

Enter **REST**: hold for various rest lengths.

TEMPO: this option is not available on this phone.

Make note **LOWER** (**FLATTEN**)

TIP: this phone can hold up to 100 notes.

DURATION: Refer to the opposite page for a list of available note and rest durations.

OCTAVES : keep pressing the up or down keys until you reach the required octave.

There are four pieces of information for every note in every tune in this book.

1. Note —— A#2 — **2.** Sharp
4. Duration —— **16** — **3.** Octave

1. Each **NOTE** name corresponds to one of the number keys on your phone (– indicates a **REST**):

1	2	3	4	5	6	7
C	**D**	**E**	**F**	**G**	**A**	**B**

Key pad equivalent:

C	D	E
F	G	A
B	↑↓	

2. If the note has a **SHARP** (#) sign after it then press ⌢ .

3. OCTAVE: Use the **8** key to move up or down one octave.

4. DURATION: Press the (key to change the duration.

Available note and rest values:

16	♪	♪
8	♪	♪
8.	use ♪ + ♪	♪ + ♪
4	♩	♪
4.	♩.	♪
2	use ♩ + ♩	♪ + ♪
2.	use ♩ + ♩ + ♩	♪ + ♪ + ♪
1	o	▬

Change Length Of Note — Up Semitone — ( ) — Down Semitone

ENTER REST
(press key until the rest is of the required length)

There is no change **TEMPO** option.

Instructions For

ERICSSON 2618, A1018, A2628, GF768, GF788e, GH688, I888, R250, R310, R320, R380, R380s, R520, S868, SH888, T10, T18, T20e, T20s, T28, T28 world, T29

There are four pieces of information for every note in every tune in this book.

1. Note — **2.** Sharp

4. Duration — A#2 **16**

3. Octave

1. Each **NOTE** name corresponds to one of the number keys on your phone (– indicates a **REST**):

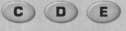

1	2	3	4	5	6	7	8	9
C	D	E	F	G	A	B	C+	D+

Key pad equivalent:

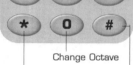

Change Octave

Rest   Sharp

2. If the note has a **SHARP** (#) sign after it then press #.

3. OCTAVE: Use the **0** key to change the octave of the note. This phone has a range of two octaves – notes in the higher octave are indicated by the + sign.

4. DURATION: Hold down the pitch keys and the length of the note will change.Only two durations are possible: short (indicated by a lower case letter) and long (indicated by an upper case letter). Dotted notes and rests of different durations are not possible.

TIP: Choose tunes with only one or two durations. For example in a tune with durations of 8 and 4, 8 would be entered as a **short** note, and 4 as a **long** one.

There are four pieces of information for every note in every tune in this book.

1. Note — A#2 — **2.** Sharp
4. Duration — **16** — **3.** Octave

1. Each **NOTE** name corresponds to one of the number keys on your phone (– indicates a **REST**):

1	2	3	4	5	6	7	-
C	D	E	F	G	A	B	REST

Key pad equivalent:

Change Octave · Shorter Duration · Longer Duration · Sharp

2. If the note has a **SHARP** (#) sign after it then press #. Press # again to cancel.

3. OCTAVE: Use the ★ key to change the octave of the note (from 1-3).

4. DURATION: Your phone will stay on the last duration you entered. **Use the 9 key to make the note longer** (e.g. to move from 4 to 2 and then on to 1). **Use the 8 key to make the note shorter** (e.g. to move from 4 to 8 and then on to 16 and 32).

If the duration has a dot (•) after it, then hold the original **NOTE** key down for longer, until the note sounds again and • appears on your display.

TEMPO: Go to the options menu and choose tempo from the list.

PRESS 8 ↓ | 1 2 4 8 16 32 | ↑ PRESS 9

13

AERODYNAMIC
By Thomas Bangalter & Guy-Manuel de Homem-Christo

D2 16	F#1 16	B1 16	F#1 16	D2 16	**TEMPO 140**
F#1 16	B1 16	F#1 16	D2 16	F#1 16	B1 16	F#1 16	D2 16	F#1 16
B1 16	F#1 16	D2 16	G#1 16	B1 16	G#1 16	D2 16	G#1 16	B1 16
G#1 16	D2 16	G#1 16	B1 16	G#1 16	D2 16	G#1 16	B1 16	G#1 16
G2 16	B2 16	E2 16	G1 16	G2 16	B2 16	E2 16	G1 16	G2 16
B1 16	E2 16	G1 16	G2 16	B1 16	E2 16	G1 16	E2 4

A LITTLE RESPECT
Words & Music by Vince Clarke & Andy Bell

C2 4.	G1 4	F1 8	E1 4.	- 8	**TEMPO 160**
E1 4	C2 4	D2 4	B1 4.	G1 4.	- 2	G1 4	A1 4	G1 4
G2 1	- 2	G2 8	E2 16	G2 8	E2 16	G2 8	A2 8	G2 2.
- 8	A2 8	G2 4.	A2 8	C3 4.	C3 2

AMERICAN PIE
Words & Music by Don McLean

D#2 8	G1 8	A#1 8	D#2 8	A#1 8		TEMPO 125
G1 8	D#1 8	G1 8	G#1 8	G1 8	D#1 8	F1 8	D#1 8	G1 8
D#1 8	A#1 8	D#1 8	G1 8	A#1 8
D#2 8	A#1 8	G1 8	D#1 8	G1 8
G#1 8	G1 8	D#1 8	F1 8	D#1 8
G1 8	D#1 8	A#1 8

...BABY ONE MORE TIME
Words & Music by Max Martin

C2 8	C2 8	C2 8	C2 4.	C2 8		TEMPO 100
B1 8	C2 8	D2 4	G1 8	F2 8	C2 8	D#2 4	D#2 8	D#2 8
D#2 8	D#2 4.	D#2 8	F2 8	G2 8	G#2 8	G2 8	- 8	C3 8
B2 8	C3 4	C2 8	C2 8	C2 8	C2 8	C2 8	C2 8	B1 8
C2 8	D2 4.	D#2 8	F2 8	G2 8	G2 2	F2 16	D#2 16	F2 16
D#2 4	- 8	G2 8	G#2 8	G2 8	G#2 8	G2 8	G#2 8	G2 4

BARBIE GIRL

Words & Music by Soren Rasted, Claus Norreen, Rene Dif,
Lene Nystrom, Johnny Pederson & Karsten Delgado

G#1 8	E1 8	G#1 8	C#2 8	A1 2				TEMPO 140
F#1 8	D#1 8	F#1 8	B1 8	G#1 4	F#1 8	E1 8	- 4	E1 8
C#1 8	F#1 4	C#1 4	- 4	F#1 8	E1 8	G#1 4	F#1 4	G#1 8
E1 8	G#1 8	C#2 8	A1 8.	A1 8	F#1 8	D#1 8	F#1 8	B1 8
G#1 4	F#1 8	E1 8	- 4	C#1 8	E1 8	C#1 8	F#1 4	C#1 4
F#1 8	F#1 8	F#1 8	E1 8	G#1 4	F#1 8	E1 8		

BLACK COFFEE

Words & Music by Tom Nichols, Alexander Soos & Kirsty Elizabeth

E2 8	F#2 8	G#2 8	G#2 8	F#2 8				TEMPO 125
G#2 4	- 4	F#2 8	G#2 8	A2 4	G#2 8	F#2 8	F#2 4	- 4
		F#2 4	F#2 16	E2 16	D2 4.	- 4		
		A1 8	E2 8	E2 8	F#2 8	F#2 8		
		E2 1.	- 8	D2 8	D2 8	E2 8		
		E2 4.	C#2 2.					

BETTER OFF ALONE

Words & Music by Eelke Kalberg & Sebastiaan Molijn

B1 / 8	- / 8	B1 / 8	G#1 / 8	- / 8	TEMPO 160
B1 / 8	- / 8	B1 / 8	- / 8	A#1 / 8	- / 8	F#1 / 8	F#2 / 8	- / 16
F#2 / 8	- / 16	D#2 / 8	B1 / 8	- / 8	B1 / 8	G#1 / 8	- / 8	B1 / 8
- / 8	B1 / 8	- / 8	A#1 / 8	- / 8	F#1 / 8	E2 / 8	- / 16	E2 / 8
- / 16	D#2 / 8				

BLUE (DA BA DEE)

Words & Music by Massimo Gabutti, Maurizio Lobina & Gianfranco Randone

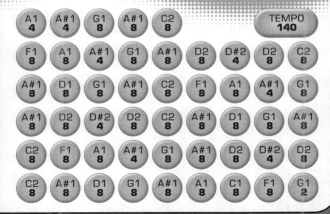

A1 / 4	A#1 / 4	G1 / 8	A#1 / 8	C2 / 8			TEMPO 140
F1 / 8	A1 / 8	A#1 / 4	G1 / 8	A#1 / 8	D2 / 8	D#2 / 4	D2 / 8	C2 / 8
A#1 / 8	D1 / 8	G1 / 8	A#1 / 8	C2 / 8	F1 / 8	A1 / 8	A#1 / 4	G1 / 8
A#1 / 8	D2 / 8	D#2 / 4	D2 / 8	C2 / 8	A#1 / 8	D1 / 8	G1 / 8	A#1 / 8
C2 / 8	F1 / 8	A1 / 8	A#1 / 8	G1 / 8	A#1 / 8	D2 / 8	D#2 / 4	D2 / 8
C2 / 8	A#1 / 8	D1 / 8	G1 / 8	A#1 / 8	A1 / 8	C1 / 8	F1 / 8	G1 / 2

BOOM, BOOM, BOOM, BOOM
Words & Music by Danski, DJ Delmundo, Benny Andersson & Björn Ulvaeus

| A#2 **4** | A#2 **4** | G#2 **4** | F#2 **4.** | C#2 **8** | | TEMPO **125** |

| C#2 **8** | C#2 **8** | G#2 **8** | G#2 **8** | F#2 **4.** |

| D#2 **8** | D#2 **8** | D#2 **8** | F#2 **8** | G#2 **8** |

| A#2 **8.** | F#2 **8.** | B1 **8** | B1 **8** | B1 **8** |

| B1 **8** | B1 **8** | A#1 **8.** | F#2 **8.** |

BRING IT ALL BACK
Words & Music by Eliot Kennedy, Mike Percy, Tim Lever & S Club 7

| G#2 **8** | - **8** | B2 **8.** | E2 **8** | E2 **16** | | TEMPO **112** |

| E2 **8** | G#2 **8.** | B1 **8** | B1 **8.** | B1 **16** | C#2 **8** | E2 **8** | F#2 **8** | E2 **8** |

| | | | | E2 **8.** | G#2 **8** | G#2 **16** | G#2 **8** |

| | | | | F#2 **8** | E2 **8** | F#2 **8** | E2 **8** |

| | | | | E2 **8.** | E2 **8** | E2 **16** | C#2 **8** |

| | | | | E2 **8** | F#2 **16** | E2 **8** |

BREATHLESS

Words & Music by R.J. Lange, Andrea Corr, Caroline Corr,
Sharon Corr & Jim Corr

E1 8	B1 8	E1 8	- 4	E1 8		TEMPO 140
B1 8	E1 4	C#1 4	- 4	C#1 8	E1 4.	D#1 4	D#1 8	E1 4
F#1 4	E1 8	E1 8	B1 8	E1 8	- 4	E1 8	B1 8	E1 8
C#1 8	- 4	C#1 8	C#1 8	E1 8	D#1 4	D#1 8	E1 4	F#1 4.
A1 8	G#1 8	F#1 8	E1 4	A1 4	E1 8	C#1 4	- 4	C#1 8
E1 4.	D#1 4	D#1 8	E1 4	F#1 4	E1 8	E1 8	B1 8	E1 8

CLINT EASTWOOD
(ED CASE/SWEETIE IRIE REFIX)

Words & Music by Damon Albarn, Jamie Hewlett, Ed Case & Sweetie Irie

D#2 16	D#2 8.	D#2 8.	A#1 8.	- 8		TEMPO 140
D#1 16	D#1 8.	F#1 8.	A#1 8.	A#1 16	A#1 8.	D#2 8.	A#1 8.	- 8
- 16	D#1 8.	F#1 8.	A#1 8.	- 8	A#1 8.	A#1 8.	A#1 8.	- 8
G#1 16	G#1 8.	F#1 8.	G#1 8.	- 8	G#1 8.	F#1 8.	D#1 8.	D#1 8
- 32	C#1 8.	D#1 8.	D#1 2

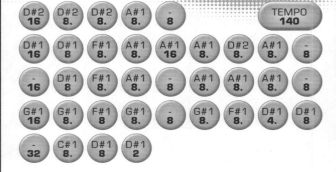

DANCING IN THE MOONLIGHT
Words & Music by Sherman Kelly

G#1 8	C2 8	D#2 8	G2 4	G2 4	TEMPO 140
F2 2	- 8	F2 32	G2 8	A#2 8	F2 8	D#2 4.	G2 8	F2 4
G2 8	F2 8	D#2 4	G2 8	A#2 8	C3 4	A#2 4	G#2 8	G#1 8
C2 8	D#2 8	G2 4	G2 4	F2 2	D2 8	F2 32	G2 8	A#2 8
F2 8	D#2 4.	G2 8	F2 4	G2 8	F2 8	D#2 2		

ETERNAL FLAME
Words & Music by Billy Steinberg, Tom Kelly & Susanna Hoffs

B1 8	C2 16	D2 2	- 16	D2 8	TEMPO 100
D2 8	E2 4.	D2 8	G1 16	A1 8	B1 8	- 8	- 16	B1 8
D2 16	G2 8.	G2 8	G2 8	G2 8	E2 8	E2 4.	E2 8	D2 8
G1 8	A1 16	B1 8.	- 8	G2 8	G2 8	F#2 4	B2 8	B2 4.
D2 8	E2 8	F#2 8	G2 8	E2 8	A2 4.	D2 8	D2 2	C3 4
B2 4	A2 8	G2 4.	C3 4	B2 4	A2 8	G2 4	D3 2	

DON'T STOP MOVIN'

Words & Music by Simon Ellis, Sheppard Solomon & S Club 7

						TEMPO 125
G2 4.	A#2 4	D2 8	F2 8	- 8		
G2 4	F2 8	C#2 8	C2 8	C2 8	A#1 8	- 4	G2 4	F2 8
D2 8	C2 8	A#1 8	C2 8	A#1 8	D2 4	- 4	F#2 4	- 4
G2 4.	A#2 4	D2 8	F2 8	- 8	G2 4	F2 8	C#2 8	C2 8
C2 8	A#1 8	- 4	C2 4	A#1 8	C2 8	A#1 8	D2 8	D2 8
- 4	G2 4	G2 4	F2 8	D2 8	C2 8	A#1 8	G1 4

GROOVEJET (IF THIS AIN'T LOVE)

Words & Music by Cristiano Spiller, Sophie Ellis-Bextor, Robert Davis, Vincent Montana Jr. & Ron Walker

						TEMPO 125
E2 8.	D2 8.	C2 8	D2 8.	C2 8.		
D2 8	E2 8.	G2 8	E2 8.	D2 8.	C2 8	D2 8.	E2 8.	D2 8.
C2 8	D2 8.	C2 8	D2 8.	A1 8	E2 8.	D2 8.	C2 8	D2 8.
C2 8.	D2 8.	E2 8	G2 8.	E2 8	D2 8.	C2 4.	A2 8.
E2 8	D2 8.	C2 8.	D2 8	A1 4	E2 8	D2 8.	E2 8.
A2 8.	G2 16	F2 2.	A2 8	A2 8	A2 4.	G2 8	G2 8	E2 2

I PUT A SPELL ON YOU

Words & Music by Screamin' Jay Hawkins

A1 16	F#1 16	E1 16	F#1 16	C#2 16	**TEMPO 125**
F#1 16	E1 16	F#1 16	A1 16	F#1 16	E1 16	F#1 16	C#2 16	F#1 16
E1 16	F#1 16	D2 16	D1 16	E1 16	D1 16	C#2 16	D1 16	E1 16
D1 16	A1 16	D1 16	E1 16	D1 16	D2 16	D1 16	E1 16	D1 16
C#2 16	D1 16	E1 16	D1 16	A1 16	D1 16	E1 16	D1 16	D2 16
D1 16	E1 16	D1 16	C#2 16	D1 16	E1 16	D1 16

INDEPENDENT WOMEN PART 1

Words & Music by Beyoncé Knowles, Samuel Barnes, Corey Rooney & Jean Claude Olivier

F#2 8	E2 16	F#2 8	A2 8	E2 16	**TEMPO 100**
F#2 8	E2 16	F#2 8	A2 8	- 16	F#2 8	E2 8	F#2 8	E2 8
F#2 8	C#2 4	B1 8	F#2 8	E2 8
F#2 8	A2 8	F#2 16	F#2 8	E2 16
F#2 8	A2 8	- 16	F#2 8	E2 8
F#2 8	E2 8	C#2 8	E2 4	F#2 8

I'M OUTTA LOVE

Words & Music by Anastacia, Sam Watters & Louis Biancaniello

					TEMPO
A1 8	A1 8	A1 8	A#1 4.	- 8	**140**

A#1 4	A#1 4	A1 4.	- 8	D#1 8	A1 8	A1 4	G#1 4	G#1 4
A#1 8	G#1 8	G1 8	G1 8.	F1 16	D#1 8	- 8	G#1 8	G#1 8
G#1 8	G#1 8	A#1 4	- 4	F1 8	A#1 4	A#1 4	A1 4	A1 8
G1 8	A1 16	G1 16	F1 4	- 8	G#1 4	G#1 4	A#1 4	C2 8
A#1 8	A#1 4						

IT FEELS SO GOOD

Words & Music by Sonique, Linus Burdick & Simon Belofsky

					TEMPO
G#1 16	G1 16	F1 4	G1 4	G#1 4	**140**

C2 4	A#1 2	- 8	G1 4	G1 4	G1 4	G1 4	F1 8	G1 8
G#1 16	A#1 16	G#1 4.	D#1 8	F1 4	- 4	C2 8	A#1 8	G#1 8
G#1 8	G#1 8	A#1 4.	A#1 2.	- 8	D#1 8	D#2 8	D#2 8	C2 8
C2 8	C2 8	A#1 8	A#1 8	G#1 4	G#1 8.	A#1 16	C2 4.	- 8
C2 4	A#1 32	C2 4	A#1 8	G#1 8	G#1 8			

LADY (HEAR ME TONIGHT)
Words & Music by Romain Tranchart, Yann Destagnol,
Nile Rodgers & Bernard Edwards

F2 8.	F2 8	- 4	D#2 8.	C#2 8			TEMPO 112
C#2 8.	C#2 8	- 4	C#2 8.	D#2 8	F2 8.	F2 8	- 4	D#2 8.
C#2 8	D#2 8.	D#2 8	- 4	C#2 8.	D#2 8	F2 4	- 4	D#2 8.
C#2 8	C#2 8	C#2 8	- 4	C#2 8.	C2 8	A#1 8.	C#2 8.	C2 8
A#1 8.	C#2 8.	C2 8	A#1 8.	C#2 8.	C2 8	A#1 8.	C#2 8.	C2 8
A#1 2

NO GOOD (START THE DANCE)
Words & Music by Liam Howlett, Kelly Charles & James Bratton

C1 8	- 8	D#1 8	- 8	G1 8		TEMPO 140
F1 16	G1 8	- 16	- 32	G1 4
G#1 8	G1 8	F1 8	F1 8	D#1 4
D#1 8	- 8	F1 8	- 8	G1 8
- 16	G#1 8.	- 8	G1 4	A#1 4
C2 8	A#1 16	C2 8

NEW BORN
Words & Music by Matthew Bellamy

B2 8	G2 8	E2 8	G2 8	B2 8			TEMPO 140
G2 8	E2 8	G2 8	B2 8	F#2 8	D#2 8	F#2 8	B2 8	F#2 8
D#2 8	F#2 8	B2 8	G2 8	E2 8	G2 8	B2 8	G2 8	E2 8
G2 8	C3 8	G2 8	E2 8	G2 8	C3 8	G2 8	E2 8	G2 8
B2 8	G2 8	D2 8	G2 8	B2 8	G2 8	D2 8	G2 8	B2 8
F#2 8	D#2 8	F#2 8	B2 8	F#2 8	D#2 8	F#2 8

OOPS!... I DID IT AGAIN
Words & Music by Max Martin & Rami

G#2 4	C#2 4	C2 8	C#2 8	D#2 8			TEMPO 112
C#2 4.	- 8	C#2 8	B1 8	D#2 8	F#2 8	E2 4.	- 8	B1 8
F#2 8	G#2 8	F#2 8	E2 4	- 4	G#2 8	F#2 8	E2 8	C#2 8
C2 8	G#2 4	C#2 4	C2 8	C#2 8	D#2 8	E2 16	D#2 16	C#2 4
- 8	B1 8	B1 8	D#2 8	F#2 8	A2 4	G#2 4	F#2 4	E2 8
- 8	E2 8	G#2 8	- 8	G#2 8	- 8	F#2 8	E2 8	C#2 8

RED ALERT

Words & Music by Simon Ratcliffe & Felix Buxton

F1 4	G1 4	G#1 4.	A#1 8	G1 4.		TEMPO 160
G#1 8	F1 2	F1 4	G1 4	G#1 4.	A#1 8	G1 4.	G#1 8	F1 2
F1 4	G#1 4	C2 4	C#2 4	C2 4	C#2 4	C2 8	A#1 8	G#1 8
- 8	G#1 8	F1 8	F1 8	A#1 1	- 4	F1 4	G#1 4	C2 4
C#2 4	C2 4	C#2 4	D#2 8	C#2 8	C2 8	- 8	G#1 8	F1 8
F1 8	A#1 1

RING, RING, RING

Words & Music by Aaron Soul & Anthony Briscoe

D#2 4	A#1 4	D#2 4	- 8	D#2 8		TEMPO 125
F2 8.	F2 8.	F2 8	F#2 16	F2 16	D#2 4.	A#2 8	A#2 16	A#2 8.
G#2 8	G#2 8	F#2 16	F#2 8.	- 8	G#2 8	G#2 16	G#2 8.	F#2 8
G#2 8	A#2 8	A#2 4	D#2 4	A#1 4	D#2 4	- 8	D#2 8	F2 8.
F2 8.	F2 8	F#2 16	F2 16	D#2 4.	A#2 8	A#2 16	A#2 8.	G#2 8
G#2 8	F#2 8	F#2 8	F2 8	F2 8	F2 8	F#2 4	F#2 4

RIGHT HERE RIGHT NOW
Words & Music by Norman Cook, Joe Walsh & Dale Peters

					TEMPO 140
A1 2.	B1 4	G1 2	F#2 2	A1 8	
B1 8	C2 8	B1 8	D2 8	C2 8	B1 8	A1 8	G1 8	A1 8
B1 8	A1 8	C2 8	B1 8	A1 8	G1 8	A1 8	B1 8	C2 8
B1 8	D2 8	C2 8	B1 8	A1 8	G1 8	A1 8	B1 8	A1 8
C2 8	B1 8	A1 8	G1 8	E2 2.	D2 4	G2 4	F#2 8	G2 8
E2 4	D2 4	E2 2.	D2 4	G2 4	F#2 8	G2 8	E2 4	D2 4

SATURDAY NIGHT
Words & Music by Alfredo Pignagnoli & Davide Riva

					TEMPO 140
B1 8	B1 8	B1 8	D#2 4	F#2 8	
F#2 8	F#2 8	G#2 8	G#2 8	G#2 8	D#2 8	F#2 4	- 4	- 2
- 8	E2 8	D#2 8	C#2 4	C#2 8	- 4	- 8	B1 8	B1 8
B1 8	D#2 4	F#2 8	F#2 8	F#2 8	G#2 8	G#2 8	G#2 8	D#2 8
F#2 4	- 2	F#2 8	E2 8	D#2 8	C#2 4	C#2 8		

...YS

Music by Craig David, Mark Hill & Darren Hill

B2 8.	B2 8	F#2 16	G2 32	F#2 32		TEMPO 80
E2 16	F#2 16	E2 16	D2 16	C2 16	B1 16	C2 8.	C2 16	B1 16
C2 16	B1 16	C2 16	D2 8	D2 16	C#2 16	D2 4	F#2 4	B2 8.
B2 8	F#2 16	G2 32	F#2 32	E2 16	F#2 16	E2 16	D2 16	C2 16
B1 16	C2 8.	C2 16	B1 16	C2 16	B1 16	C2 16	D2 8.	D2 8
C#2 16	D2 16	F#2 4.

STRONGER

Words & Music by Max Martin & Rami

C#2 8	D#2 4	F#2 8	G#2 8	G#2 4.		TEMPO 125
G#2 4	- 8	D#2 8	F#2 4.	G#2 8	D#2 4.	- 4	G#2 4	G#2 4
G#2 8	G#2 8	G#2 8	D#2 8	F#2 4.	D#2 8	C#2 4	B1 4	B2 4
F#2 8	E2 4	D#2 4	G#2 8	F#2 8	F#2 8	D#2 4	F#2 4	D#2 8
C#2 8	D#2 8	E2 16	D#2 16	C#2 2	- 4	- 8	G#2 2	A#2 2
G#2 4.	G#2 4.

STOMP

Words & Music by Mark Topham, Karl Twigg & Rita Campbell

A1 8	C2 8	A#1 4	A1 8	G1 8			TEMPO 140
F1 8	G1 4	- 4	G1 16	G1 8	A1 8.	D1 8	D1 4	- 4
- 8	D1 8	F1 8	G1 8	A1 4	G1 8	F1 8	G1 4	A1 4
- 8	A1 8	C2 8	A#1 4	A1 8	G1 8	F1 8	G1 4	- 8
D1 8	G1 8	G1 8	A1 8	C1 16	D1 8.	- 4	- 16	D1 8
F1 8	G1 8	A1 4	G1 8	F1 8	G1 4	F1 4		

SURVIVOR

Words & Music by Beyoncé Knowles, Anthony Dent & Matthew Knowles

G#1 8	D#1 8	G#1 8	A#1 8	B1 8			TEMPO 160
A#1 8	G#1 8	D#1 8	E1 8	G#1 8	B1 8	E2 8	B1 8	G#1 8
E1 8	G#1 8	D#1 8	G1 8	A#1 8	C#2 8	A#1 8	G1 8	D#1 8
G1 8	G#1 8	D#1 8	G#1 8	A#1 8	D#1 8	G1 8	A#1 8	D#2 8

(MUCHO MAMBO) SWAY
Original Words & Music by Pablo Beltran Ruiz
English Words by Norman Gimbel

| C2 8 | C2 8 | C2 8 | C2 8 | C2 8 | | | | TEMPO 160 |

| C2 8 | C#2 4 | C2 8 | A#1 4. | - 4 | C#2 4 | C2 8 | A#1 4. | - 4 |

| C2 4 | A#1 8 | G#1 4. | - 2 | G#1 8 | G#1 8 | G#1 8 | G#1 8 | G#1 8 |

| G#1 8 | A#1 8 | G#1 4. | G1 4 | - 4 | A#1 4 | G#1 8 | G1 4. | - 4 |

| G#1 4 | G1 8 | F1 4. | - 2 | C2 8 | C2 4 | C2 8 | C2 4 | C2 8 |

| F2 1 |

THE REAL SLIM SHADY
Words & Music by Marshall Mathers, Andre Young,
Mike Elizondo & Thomas Coster

| C1 4 | D#1 4 | G1 4 | G#1 4 | C2 4 | | | | TEMPO 200 |

| - 2 | G#1 4 | G1 4 | 2 | G#1 4 | G1 16 | G#1 16 | G1 16 | F1 4 |

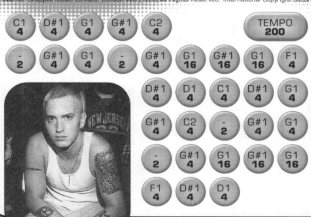

| | | D#1 4 | D1 4 | C1 4 | D#1 4 | G1 4 |

| | | G#1 4 | C2 4 | - 2 | G#1 4 | G1 4 |

| | | - 2 | G#1 4 | G1 16 | G#1 16 | G1 16 |

| | | F1 4 | D#1 4 | D1 4 | | |

THAT DON'T IMPRESS ME MUCH
Words & Music by Shania Twain & R.J. Lange

F2 8	F2 8	C#2 8	D#2 8	A#1 8		TEMPO 125
C#2 4	C#2 4.	D#2 8	- 8	D#2 4	D#2 8	F2 4	F2 8	C#2 4
D#2 8	C#2 4	F2 8	F2 8	D#2 8	C#2 8	- 8	D#2 8	C#2 8
F2 4.	- 8	C#2 8	G#2 8	A#2 8	G#2 8	C#3 4.	F2 8	C#2 8
D#2 8	A#1 4	C#2 8	C#2 4.	A#1 8	G#2 8	A#2 8	A#2 8	G#2 8
G#2 8	F2 8	C#2 8	D#2 4	D#2 8	D#2 8	C#2 8	D#2 8	F2 8

THINGS I'VE SEEN
Words & Music by Booker T. Tucker, Joseph M. Davis, Chenjerai Kumanyika, Jerel Spruill, Irina M. Perez & Rick Dahrouge

G#1 16	E2 8	C#2 16	C#2 8	G#1 8		TEMPO 100
E2 8	C#2 8	C#2 4	- 16	E2 8	C#2 16	C#2 8	A1 8	E2 8
C#2 8	C#2 4	G#1 16	D#2 8
C2 16	C2 8	G#1 8	D#2 8
G#1 8	G#1 8	F#1 8	G#1 16
A1 8	G#1 2

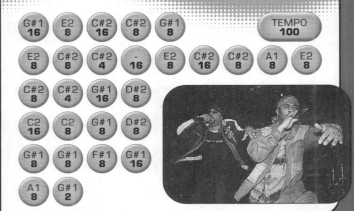

TOCA'S MIRACLE

Words & Music by Ramon Zenker, Dirk Duderstadt,
Marco Duderstadt, Victor Imbres & Robert Davis

D1 8	E1 8	E1 8	D1 8	E1 4		TEMPO 140
- 8	D1 8	E1 4	- 8	D1 8	E1 8	G1 8	- 4	G1 4
G1 8	A1 8	G1 8	F#1 8	E1 8	- 8	G1 4	G1 8	A1 8
G1 8	F#1 8	E1 8	- 8	A1 8	A1 8	G1 8	A1 8	A1 8
A1 8	G1 8	A1 8	B1 4	B1 16	C2 16	B1 4	D2 4	A1 4
G1 8	A1 16	G1 4.

WHAT TOOK YOU SO LONG?

Words & Music by Emma Bunton, Richard Stannard,
Julian Gallagher, Martin Harrington, John Themis & Dave Morgan

A1 8	C2 8	C2 8	D2 4	E2 4		TEMPO 125
- 8	A1 8	C2 4	D2 4	E2 4	- 8	A1 8	C2 4	D2 8
E2 4	D2 8	D2 8	D2 8	B1 4	G1 8	- 8	A1 8	C2 8
A1 8	C2 8	D2 4	E2 4	- 8	A1 8	C2 8	D2 4	E2 4
- 8	A1 8	A1 8	A1 8	A2 4	G2 8	G2 8	G2 8	G2 8
E2 4	D2 4	E2 8	- 4	E2 8	D2 8	C2 8	D2 8	C2 8

AIN'T TALKIN' 'BOUT LOVE

Words & Music by Edward Van Halen, Alex Van Halen, David Lee Roth & Michael Anthony

B1 8	D2 8	F#2 8	D2 8	F#2 8	**TEMPO 160**
G2 8	D2 8	C#2 8	A2 8	E2 8	
C#2 8	D2 4.	C#2 8	B1 8	D2 8	
F#2 8	D2 8	F#2 8	G2 8	D2 8	
C#2 8	A2 8	E2 8	C#2 8	D2 4.	
C#2 4					

ANIMAL NITRATE

Words & Music by Brett Anderson & Bernard Butler

D2 8	E2 8	D2 8	F#2 4	E2 8	**TEMPO 112**
D2 2	- 8	F#2 4	E2 8	D2 2.	D2 4	G2 8	G2 4	D2 2.

D2 8	D2 8	D2 8	F#2 4	E2 8
D2 2	- 8	F#2 4	E2 8	D2 2
- 8	F#2 4	D2 4	G2 8	F#2 8
D2 8	D2 4	B1 2

APACHE

By Jerry Lordan

A1 8	C2 8	D2 8	D#2 8	D2 2				TEMPO 160
A1 8	C2 8	A2 8	G2 8	E2 8	E1 8	A1 2	E1 4	A1 4
F#1 2	E1 4	D1 4	E1 1	- 2	- 4	E1 4	A1 2	E1 4
A1 4	F#1 2	E1 4	D1 4	E1 1	- 2	- 4	A1 4	D2 2
A1 4	D2 4	B1 2	A1 4	G1 4	A1 1	- 2	- 4	E1 4
A1 2	E1 4	A1 4	F#1 2	E1 4	D1 4			

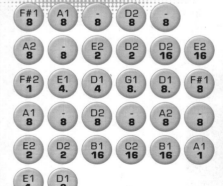

BORDERLINE

Words & Music by Reggie Lucas

F#1 8	A1 8	- 8	D2 8	- 8		TEMPO 125
A2 8	- 8	E2 2	D2 2	D2 16	E2 16	
F#2 1	E1 4.	D1 4	G1 8.	D1 8.	F#1 8	
A1 8	- 8	D2 8	- 8	A2 8	- 8	
E2 2	D2 2	B1 16	C2 16	B1 16	A1 1	
E1 4.	D1 2					

BAKER STREET
Words & Music by Gerry Rafferty

A1 8	F2 8	E2 4	D2 16	C2 16				TEMPO 140
D2 1	- 4	- 8	F1 8	F2 8	E2 4	D2 16	C2 16	A1 1
- 4	- 8	A1 8	F2 8	E2 4	D2 16	C2 16	C2 4.	C2 4.
C2 4.	B1 32	C2 8	A1 4.	A1 8	F2 8	E2 4	D2 16	C2 16
D2 4.	G1 8	F1 8	D1 4.	C1 16	D1 8.	D1 4		

BROWN EYED GIRL
Words & Music by Van Morrison

B1 8	C2 4	D2 4	C2 8	B1 4				TEMPO 160
E2 8	F2 4	G2 4	F2 8	E2 4	B1 8	C2 4	D2 4	C2 8
B1 4	A1 1	B1 8	C2 4	D2 4	C2 8	B1 4	E2 8	F2 4
G2 4	F2 8	E2 4	B1 8	C2 4	D2 4	C2 8	B1 4	A1 1

CARELESS WHISPER
Words & Music by George Michael & Andrew Ridgeley

| F2 8 | C3 32 | D3 32 | E3 8 | D3 16 | | TEMPO 70 |

A2 8	F2 8	E3 8.	D3 16	A2 8	F2 8.
C3 8	A#2 16	F2 8	D2 8	C3 8	A#2 16
F2 4	- 16	A#2 8	A2 16	F2 8	D2 8
A#1 2	- 16	A1 8	A#1 8	C2 8	D2 8
E2 8	F2 8	G2 8	A2 8		

COPACABANA (AT THE COPA)
Words & Music by Barry Manilow, Bruce Sussman & Jack Feldman

| G1 8 | A#1 8 | C2 8 | D#2 8. | G#1 4. | | TEMPO 125 |

- 16	D#2 8	D2 8	C2 8	D2 8.	G1 4.	- 16	G1 8	A#1 8
C2 8	D2 8	D#2 8	D2 8	D#2 16	D2 4	- 16	A#1 8	F1 8
G1 8	A1 8	A#1 8	C2 8	D2 8	A#1 8	G1 8	D1 8	F#1 8.
A1 8.	G1 4	A#1 8	G1 8	D1 8	F#1 8.	A1 8.	A#1 8.	

CARS

Words & Music by Gary Numan

| D2 8 | C#2 8 | G1 8 | A1 4 | A1 8 | | TEMPO 140 |

| - 4 | D2 8 | C#2 8 | G1 8 | A1 4 | A1 8 | - 4 | D2 8 | C#2 8 |

| G1 8 | A1 4 | A1 4 | - 4 | D2 8 |

| C#2 8 | G1 8 | A1 4 | A1 8 | A1 8 |

| F#1 8 | G1 4 | B1 8 | G1 8 | - 8 |

| - 4 | F#1 8 | G1 4 | B1 8 | G1 8 |

DANCING QUEEN

Words & Music by Benny Andersson, Björn Ulvaeus & Stig Anderson

| C#2 2. | B1 4 | D2 2. | C#2 16 | B1 8 | | | TEMPO 125 |

| A1 16 | B1 8. | C#2 2 | - 16 | B1 4 | A1 4. | A1 2 | - 8 | C#2 4 |

| B1 8 | B1 4. | - 4 | C#2 4 | B1 4 | B1 4 | C#2 4 | A1 8. | B1 8. |

| G#1 8 | A1 8. | B1 8. | G#1 8 | A1 16 | G#1 16 | F#1 4. | C#2 8. | B1 8. |

| A1 8 | G#1 8. | A1 8. | A1 2 | - 8 | G#1 8. | A1 8. | A1 4. | B1 16 |

| A1 8 | G#1 16 | G#1 8. | A1 8. | A1 2 |

DAY TRIPPER
Words & Music by John Lennon & Paul McCartney

C1 4.	D#1 8	E1 8	G1 8	C2 8			TEMPO 160
A#1 4.	G1 8	D2 4	G1 8	A#1 8	C2 8	C1 4.	D#1 8	E1 8
G1 8	C2 8	A#1 4.	G1 8	D2 4	G1 8	A#1 8	C2 8	F1 4.
G#1 8	A1 8	C2 8	F2 8	D#2 4.	C2 8	G2 4	C2 8	D#2 8
F2 8	C1 4.	D#1 8	E1 8	G1 8	C2 8	A#1 4.	G1 8	D2 4
G1 8	A#1 8	C2 8					

EVERY BREATH YOU TAKE
Words & Music by Sting

C2 8	D#2 8	G#2 8	D#2 8	C3 8			TEMPO 125
A#2 8	G#2 8	A#2 8	C2 8	D#2 8	G#2 8	D#2 8	C3 8	A#2 8
G#2 8	A#2 8	G#1 8	C2 8	G2 8	C2 8	G#2 8	G2 8	F2 8
G2 8	G#1 8	C2 8	G2 8	C2 8	G#2 8	G2 8	F2 8	G2 8
F2 8	G#2 8	D#3 8	G#2 8	C#3 8	G#2 8	C3 8	A#2 8	G2 8
A#2 8	F3 8	A#2 8	D#3 8	A#2 8	C#3 8	D#3 8	G#2 4	

A DESIGN FOR LIFE

Words & Music by Nicky Wire, James Dean Bradfield & Sean Moore

D1 4.	F1 4.	A1 4	A1 8	B1 4.				TEMPO 100
B1 2.	- 2	D1 4.	F1 4	F1 8	A1 4	A1 8	B1 4.	B1 2.
- 2	B1 8	B1 8	A1 4	B1 8	C2 4.	B1 4.	A1 8	E1 4.
G1 8	G1 4.	F1 4.	C1 4.	D1 4.	G1 4.	F1 4	C1 8	C1 2.
B1 4.	A1 4.	E1 2.	G1 4.	F1 4.	C1 2.	B1 4.	A1 4.	E1 2.
G1 4.	F1 4.	C1 2.	F1 4.	F1 4.	F1 4.	G1 4.	E1 4.	

F.B.I.

By Hank Marvin, Bruce Welch & Jet Harris

A1 8.	C2 16	D2 8	E2 4.	- 8				TEMPO 125
A1 8	D2 8.	C2 16	A1 2	- 4	A1 8.	C2 16	D2 8	E2 4.
- 4	A1 8.	D2 8.	C2 16	A1 2	- 4	A1 8.	C2 16	A2 4
G2 8.	E2 16	D2 4	C2 8.	D2 16	E2 8.	E2 16	D2 8.	C2 16
A1 4	A1 8.	C2 16	D2 8.	E2 16	D2 8.	C2 16	D2 8.	E2 16
D2 8.	C2 16	D2 16.	E2 16.	D2 16.	C2 16	A1 16	A1 4	

THE FINAL COUNTDOWN
Words & Music by Joey Tempest

C#3 16	B2 16	C#3 4	F#2 4.	- 4			TEMPO 125
D3 16	C#3 16	D3 8	C#3 8	B2 4.	- 4	D3 16	C#3 16	D3 4
F#2 4.	- 4	B2 16	A2 16	B2 8	A2 8	G#2 8	B2 8	A2 4.
G#2 16	A2 16	B2 4.	A2 16	B2 16	C#3 8	B2 8	A2 8	G#2 8
F#2 4	D3 4	C#3 2.	C#3 16	D3 16	C#3 16	B2 16	C#3 2	

GHOST TOWN
Words & Music by Jerry Dammers

G#2 32	G2 2	G2 8.	G#2 16	B2 16		TEMPO 90
C3 16	B2 16	G#2 16	G2 1	C2 8	G2 16	F#2 2	F2 8.	D#2 8
		D2 1	G#2 32	G2 2	G2 8.	G#2 16	B2 16
C3 16	B2 16	G#2 16	G2 1	G2 4.	F2 8
C#2 4	C2 4	B1 4	E2 16	E2 8	G#2 8
G#2 8	G#2 16	B2 8	E3 8

GET BACK

Words & Music by John Lennon & Paul McCartney

C2 / 8	C2 / 8	C2 / 8	C2 / 8	C2 / 4		TEMPO 125
D2 / 4	D#2 / 8	D#2 / 8	D#2 / 8	D#2 / 8	D2 / 8	C2 / 8	- / 8	A#1 / 4
A#1 / 8	A#1 / 8	A#1 / 8	F1 / 8	D1 / 4	C1 / 2.	- / 4	D#2 / 8	D#2 / 2.
- / 8	D#2 / 8	D#2 / 2.	- / 8	D#2 / 8	D#2 / 8	D2 / 4	D2 / 8	C2 / 8
C2 / 4	G#1 / 8	G1 / 8	F1 / 2	- / 4	D#2 / 8	D#2 / 2.	- / 8	D#2 / 8
D#2 / 4	D2 / 8	D2 / 8	C2 / 8	C2 / 4	G#1 / 8	G1 / 8	F1 / 2.

GIMME! GIMME! GIMME! (A MAN AFTER MIDNIGHT)

Words & Music by Benny Andersson & Björn Ulvaeus

D2 / 32	F2 / 32	A2 / 16	D3 / 8	D3 / 32		TEMPO 112
A2 / 32	F2 / 16	D2 / 2	- / 8	D2 / 32	F2 / 32	A2 / 16	D3 / 8	D3 / 32
A2 / 32	F2 / 16	D2 / 16	E2 / 16	F2 / 16	G2 / 16	A2 / 4.	F2 / 32	A2 / 32
C3 / 16	F3 / 8	F3 / 32	E3 / 32	C3 / 16
A2 / 2	- / 8	E2 / 32	A2 / 32	C3 / 16
E3 / 8	D3 / 32	A2 / 32	F2 / 16	D2 / 2

GOOD TIMES
Words & Music by Bernard Edwards & Nile Rodgers

E1 4	E1 4	E1 4	- 4	E1 16.		TEMPO 112
E1 32.	F#1 8	G1 8	A1 8	B1 8
C#2 8	D2 8	E2 16	A1 4	- 16
A1 4	A1 4	- 8	A1 16	F#2 8
A1 16	F#2 16	A1 16	F#2 8	F#2 8
A1 8

HEY JUDE
Words & Music by John Lennon & Paul McCartney

C2 4	A1 2	- 8	A1 8	C2 8			TEMPO 90
D2 8	G1 2	- 4	G1 8	A1 8	A#1 4	F2 4.	F2 8	E2 8
C2 8	D2 8	C2 16	A#1 16	A1 2	- 8	C2 8	D2 8	D2 4
D2 8	G2 16	F2 8	E2 16	F2 8	D2 8	C2 2	F1 8	G1 8
A1 8	D2 4	C2 8	- 8	C2 8	A#1 8	A1 8	E1 8	E1 4
F1 2	A1 4	C2 4	G2 16.	F2 32	G2 8	F2 2	D2 4	C2 2

A HAZY SHADE OF WINTER

Words & Music by Paul Simon

D2 8	D2 8	F2 8	G2 8	A2 8		TEMPO 160
G2 8	F2 4	C2 8	G2 8	C3 4.	A#2 4	G2 8	A#1 8	A#1 8
D2 8	F2 8	G#2 8	G2 8	F2 4	A1 8	E2 8	A2 8	G2 4.
A2 4	D2 8	D2 8	F2 8	G2 8	A2 8	G2 8	F2 8	C2 4
G2 8	C3 8	A#2 4.	G2 4	A#1 8	A#1 8	D2 8	F2 8	G#2 8
G2 8	F2 8	A1 4	E2 8	A2 8	G2 4.	A2 4		

I SHOULD BE SO LUCKY

Words & Music by Mike Stock, Matt Aitken & Pete Waterman

C2 4	C2 8	A1 8	E1 8	G1 8		TEMPO 140
A1 4	G1 4	A1 8	G1 8	A1 8	G1 8	A1 4	C2 4	C2 8
A1 8	E1 8	G1 8	A1 4	G1 8.	F1 16	E1 2	- 4	- 16
C2 4	C2 8	A1 8	E1 8	G1 8	A1 4	C2 4	A1 8	C2 8
A1 8	C2 8	G1 8	A1 8	C2 4	C2 8	A1 8	G1 8	C2 8
C2 4	A1 8	G1 2						

I WILL SURVIVE
Words & Music by Dino Fekaris & Freddie Perren

G#1 8	G#1 8	A1 4.	- 4	A1 8		TEMPO 112
B1 8	C2 16	B1 8	A1 4.	- 16	A1 8.	A1 8	A1 8	G1 8
G1 8	G1 8	A1 8	G1 16	G1 8.	G1 8	A1 8	G1 8	G1 16
G1 16	G1 4.	E1 4	E1 8	E1 8	E1 8	E1 16	E1 4	- 16
E1 8	E1 8	E1 8	E1 8	F1 8	E1 16	E1 4	E1 16	E1 8
E1 16	E1 4	- 2	E1 8	A1 8	F#1 16	G#1 2	G#1 4	A1 4.

ISRAELITES
Words & Music by Desmond Dacres & Leslie Kong

A#1 8	A#1 8	A#1 8	A#1 8	A#1 8		TEMPO 140
A#1 4	A#1 4	A#1 4	A#1 4	G#1 4	C2 4	- 4	A#1 8	A#1 8
D2 8	D2 8	D#2 8	F2 4	F2 8	A#2 4	D2 16	C2 16	A#1 4
- 2	G1 8	A#1 4	G1 8	A1 4.	A#1 2	C2 4	- 8	A1 8
A#1 4	A#1 8	A#1 4.						

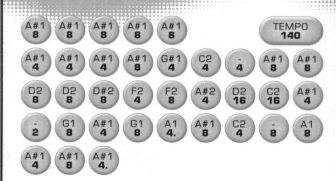

I WISH IT COULD BE CHRISTMAS EVERY DAY

Words & Music by Roy Wood

G2 4	A2 4	B2 4	C3 4	B2 4			TEMPO 160
A2 8	G2 4	A2 4.	- 8	G2 8	D2 8	F2 4	E2 16	D2 16
E2 2.	- 2	- 4	G2 8.	G2 16	F#2 4	G2 4	F#2 8.	F#2 16
E2 8.	E2 16	D2 4	E2 8	D2 4.	C2 4	E2 4	F#2 8	D2 2
- 2	- 8	G2 8	G2 8.	A2 16	B2 2.	B2 4	A2 2.	B2 4
A2 4	G2 2.

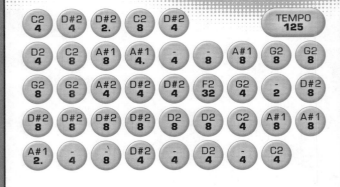

IT'S MY LIFE

Words & Music by Jon Bon Jovi, Richie Sambora & Max Martin

C2 4	D#2 4	D#2 2.	C2 8	D#2 4			TEMPO 125
D2 4	C2 8	A#1 8	A#1 4.	- 4	- 8	A#1 8	G2 8	G2 8
G2 8	G2 8	A#2 8	D#2 8	D#2 8	F2 32	G2 4	- 2	D#2 8
D#2 8	D#2 8	D#2 8	D#2 8	D2 8	D2 8	C2 4	A#1 8	A#1 8
A#1 2.	- 4	` 8	D#2 4	- 4	D2 4	- 4	C2 4

KILLING ME SOFTLY

Words by Norman Gimbel
Music by Charles Fox

© Copyright 1972 Fox-Gimbel Productions Incorporated, USA. Onward Music Limited, London W8 for the British Commonwealth (excluding Canada), the Republic of South Africa and the Republic of Ireland. All Rights Reserved. International Copyright Secured.

G2 4	G2 8	G2 4	E2 8	B1 8				TEMPO 125
D2 4	C2 2	- 4	- 8	F#2 8	F#2 8	F#2 8	F#2 4	D2 8
A1 8	B1 2.	- 4	B1 4	B1 8	B1 4	E2 8	G2 8	F#2
E2 4.	A2 8	A2 8	A2 8	G2 4	F#2 4.	- 4	D2 4	F#2 4
E2 4.	E2 4	G2 8	E2 4	D2 4.	- 4	G1 8	D2 4	C2 4.
C2 8	C2 8	B1 4.	B1 8	A1 2.	- 2	A1 4	A1 4	B1 1

LAST RESORT

Words & Music by Papa Roach

© Copyright 2000 Viva La Cucaracha Music/DreamWorks Songs, USA. Worldwide rights for Viva La Cucaracha Music and DreamWorks Songs administered by Cherry Lane Music Publishing Company Incorporated, USA. All Rights Reserved. International Copyright Secured.

E2 8	E2 8	E2 8	G2 8	G2 8			TEMPO 100
D2 8	D2 8	- 8	E2 8	E2 8	E2 8	G2 8	A2 8	D2 4
E2 16	G2 16	F#2 16	G2 16	B2 16	F#2 16	G2 16	D2 16
G2 16	F#2 16	G2 16	B2 16	G2 16	F#2 16	C2 16	G2 16
F#2 16	G2 16	B2 16	G2 16	F#2 16	G2 16	B1 16	G2 16	F#2 16
G2 16	B2 16	G2 16	F#2 16	G2 16			

LADY MARMALADE
Words & Music by Bob Crewe & Kenny Nolan

G1 8	A#1 8	A1 8	G1 4	A#1 8			TEMPO 125
A1 8	G1 4	A#1 8	A1 8	G1 16	A1 16	A#1 8.	- 4	G1 8
A#1 8	A1 8	G1 4	A#1 8	A1 4	A1 16	G1 16	F1 4	- 2
A#1 8	A#1 8	A#1 8	G1 8	G1 4	G1 4	A1 4	F1 4	- 2
A#1 8	A#1 8	A#1 8	G1 8	G1 4	G1 4	A1 8.	G1 16	F1 4
- 2	C2 8	A#1 8	C2 8	D2 8	C2 8	A#1 8	G1 8	G1 2

LAYLA
Words & Music by Eric Clapton & Jim Gordon

A#1 16	C#2 16	D#2 16	F#2 16	D#2 16			TEMPO 125
C#2 16	D#2 4.	G#2 4	F#2 4	F2 4	C#2 4	D#2 4	A#1 16	C#2 16
D#2 16	F#2 16	D#2 16	C#2 16	D#2 4.	A#2 4	G#2 4	F2 4	C#2 4
D#2 4	A#1 16	C#2 16	D#2 16	F#2 16	D#2 16	C#2 16	D#2 4.	G#2 4
F#2 4	F2 4	C#2 4	D#2 4	A#1 16	C#2 16	D#2 16	F#2 16	D#2 16
C#2 16	D#2 4.	A#2 4	G#2 4	F2 4	C#2 4	D#2 4		

LIGHT MY FIRE
Words & Music by Jim Morrison, Robbie Krieger, Ray Manzarek & John Densmore

B2 8	G2 16	A2 16	B2 8	D3 8			TEMPO 125
C3 8	B2 8	A2 8	G2 8	A2 16	F2 16	A2 8	C3 8	F3 8
D3 16	C3 16	A#2 16	G2 16	G#2 8	G#2 8	G#2 16	G2 16	G#2 8
A#2 8	C3 8	A#2 16	G#2 16	G2 16	F2 16	D#2 8	F2 8	A2 8
C#2 8	E2 8	A2 8	C#2 8	E2 8	A2 8	E2 8	A2 4	C#2 8
A2 8	E2 8	C#2 8	E2 8	A2 8

LIVE FOREVER
Words & Music by Noel Gallagher

D2 8.	B1 2	- 8	G1 16	D2 8			TEMPO 90
B1 16	A1 16	A1 16	G1 16	A1 2	- 16	D1 16	D1 16	A1 8.
A1 8	A1 2	- 8	D1 16	A1 8.	A1 8	A1 8	G1 16	A1 2
- 16	D2 8.	B1 2	- 16	D2 8.	D2 16	B1 16	A1 16	A1 16
G1 16	A1 2	- 16	D1 16	D1 16	B1 16	A1 8	A1 8	A1 2
- 16	D1 16	D1 16	B1 16	A1 8	A1 8	A1 8	G1 16	A1 2

LIKE A VIRGIN

Words & Music by Billy Steinberg & Tom Kelly

C1 8	D1 8	F1 4	D1 4	- 4				TEMPO 125
F2 4	- 2	G1 4	G1 8	F1 8	G1 8	G1 8	C2 4	A1 2
- 2	- 4	C1 8	D1 8	A1 8	G1 4	F1 8	G1 8	D1 2.
- 8	F1 8	G1 8	F1 4	D1 4	- 2	A1 8	F1 8	G1 8
F1 4	G1 8	F1 8	E1 8	D2 2	- 2	- 2	F1 8	G1 8
F1 8	E1 8	D1 32	E1 4	D1 2				

LOVE CATS

Words & Music by Robert Smith

G1 16	G1 8	A1 8	- 8	E2 8				TEMPO 100
- 8	D2 8	- 16	C2 8	C2 16	G1 8	F1 8	- 8	D2 8
- 8	C2 8	- 16	B1 8	B1 16	G1 8	A1 8	- 8	E2 8
- 8	D2 8	- 16	C2 8	C2 16	G1 8	F1 8	- 8	D2 8
- 8	C2 8	- 16	B1 8	B1 16	G1 8	A1 8		

LOVEFOOL
Words & Music by Peter Svensson & Nina Persson

A1 4	F#1 8	A1 4	F#1 4	C#2 4			TEMPO 160
B1 4	A1 8	G#1 4	E1 4	G#1 4	E1 8	G#1 4	E1 4	G#1 4
A1 4	G#1 8	A1 4	B1 4	A1 4	F#1 4	A1 4	F#1 4	A1 4
C#2 4	B1 4	A1 8	G#1 4	E1 4	G#1 4	E1 8	G#1 4	E1 4
F#1 8	G#1 4	A1 4	G#1 8	A1 4	B1 4	A1 4	F#1 4	A1 8.
F1 16	F1 4	E1 4	F#1 4	G#1 4	B1 4	A1 1

MADE OF STONE
Words & Music by John Squire & Ian Brown

E1 8	D3 8	G2 8	E2 8	D3 8			TEMPO 125
G2 8	E2 8	G2 8	E1 8	C#3 8	G2 8	E2 8	C#3 8	G2 8
		E2 8	G2 8	E1 8	C3 8	G2 8
		E2 8	C3 8	G2 8	E2 8	G2 8
		E1 8	B2 8	G2 8	E2 8	B2 8
		G2 8	F#2 16	G2 16	F#2 8	

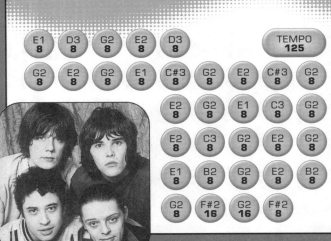

LUCY IN THE SKY WITH DIAMONDS
Words & Music by John Lennon & Paul McCartney

E1	A1	E2	G1	E2		TEMPO
4	4	4	4	4		140

A1	F#1	A1	E2	F1	D2	C#2	A1	E1
4	4	4	4	4	8	8	4	4

A1	E2	G1	E2	A1	F#1	A1	E2	C2
4	4	4	4	4	4	4	4	4

A1	C2	C2
4	4	2.

MESSAGE IN A BOTTLE
Words & Music by Sting

C#2	G#2	D#3	A1	E2		TEMPO
8	8	8	4	8		140

B2	B1	F#2	C#3	F#1	C#2	G#2	A2	C#2
8	4	8	8	4	8	8	8	8

G#2	D#3	A1	E2	B2	B1	F#2	C#3	F#1
8	8	4	8	8	4	8	8	4

C#2	G#2	A2
8	8	8

MONEY, MONEY, MONEY (CHORUS)
Words & Music by Benny Andersson & Björn Ulvaeus

E2 8	F2 8	D2 8	E2 8	C2 8		TEMPO 140
D2 8	B1 8	E2 8	F2 8	D2 8	E2 8	C2 8	D2 8	B1 8
C2 4	A2 8	B2 8	C3 8	A2 8	B2 8	C3 8	E1 8	D#1 4.
C3 8	A2 8	B2 8	C3 8	D#1 8	D1 4.	B2 8	A2 8	C3 8
C3 4	A2 4.	- 4	A2 16	B2 16	C3 16	E3 16	A3 16	

MRS. ROBINSON
Words & Music by Paul Simon

A1 4	A#1 4	C2 8	D2 8.	- 4		TEMPO 200
D2 8	D#2 4	D2 4	C2 4	A#1 4.	- 4	F2 8	D2 4.	D2 8
D#2 4	D2 4	C2 4	A#1 4.	C2 4	A#1 1.	D#2 8	D2 4	C2 2.
- 2	A1 4	A#1 4	C2 4	D2 2	D2 8	D#2 4	D2 4	C2 4
A#1 4.	- 4	F2 8	D2 4	D2 4	D#2 4	D2 4	C2 4.	A#1 4
C2 4	A#1 1.	D#2 8	D2 4	C2 1.	C2 4	C2 4	B1 1.	

MONEY, MONEY, MONEY (INTRO)
Words & Music by Benny Andersson & Björn Ulvaeus

E2 8	E2 8	E2 8	E2 8	E2 8		TEMPO 140
E2 8	E1 16	A1 16	C2 16	E2 16	D#2 8	D#2 8	D#2 8	D#2 8
D#2 8	D#2 8	F1 16	A1 16	C2 16	D#2 16	D2 4	C2 8	A1 8
C2 8	C2 4	A1 2	A2 8	- 8	- 8	A1 16	B1 16	C2 16
E2 16	A1 16	B1 16	C2 16	E2 16	A1 16	B1 16	C2 16	E2 16
A1 16	B1 16	C2 16	E2 16

ONLY YOU
Words & Music by Vince Clarke

C#2 8	C#2 8	C#2 8	C#2 8	D2 8		TEMPO 112
C#2 8	B1 8	A1 4	A1 8	A1 8	A1 8	G#1 8	A1 8	G#1 8
F#1 2	- 4	C#2 8	C#2 4	C#2 4.	B1 8	B1 4	- 4	C#2 8
C#2 8	C#2 8	C#2 8	D2 8	C#2 4	A1 4	A1 8	A1 8	A1 8
G#1 8	A1 8	G#1 8	F#1 2	- 4	D2 8	D2 4	C#2 4.	B1 8
B1 2

PLUG IN BABY
Words & Music by Matthew Bellamy

A#1 8	B1 8	C#2 8	A#1 8	B1 8	**TEMPO 125**
C#2 8	D2 8	B1 8	C#2 8	D2 8	E2 8 · F#2 16 · G2 16 · F#2 8
E2 8	D2 8	C#2 8	B1 8	C#2 8	D2 8 · B1 8 · C#2 8 · D2 8
E2 8	C#2 8	D2 8	E2 8	F#2 8	F#2 16 · G2 16 · F#2 8 · F2 8
F#2 8	F2 8	F#2 8	D2 8	A1 8	F#1 8 · A1 8 · D2 8 · F#2 8
G#2 8	A2 8	G#2 8	F#2 8	F2 8	F#2 8 · D2 8 · C#2 8 · D2 8

RUN TO YOU
Words & Music by Bryan Adams & Jim Vallance

F#1 8	C#2 8	E2 8	F#1 8	C#2 8 · **TEMPO 140**
E2 8	C#2 8	F#1 8	A1 8	C#2 8 · E2 8
B1 8	D#2 8	E2 8	D#2 8	B1 8 · F#1 8
C#2 8	E2 8	F#1 8	C#2 8	E2 8 · C#2 8
F#1 8	A1 8	C#2 8	E2 8	B1 8 · D#2 8
E2 8	D#2 8	B1 8		

THE RIVERBOAT SONG

**Words & Music by Simon Fowler, Steve Cradock,
Oscar Harrison & Damon Minchella**

B1 8.	D2 8	E2 16	B1 8	D2 8	**TEMPO 112**
E2 8	B1 8.	D2 8	E2 16	B1 8	D2 8	E2 8	E2 8.	G2 8
A2 16	E2 8	G2 8	A2 8	E2 8.	G2 8	A2 16	E2 8	G2 8
A2 8	B1 8.	D2 8	E2 16	B1 8	D2 8	E2 8	B1 8.	D2 8
E2 16	B1 8	D2 8	E2 8	F#2 8.	A2 8	B2 16	F#2 8	A2 8
B2 8	F#2 8.	A2 8	B2 16	F#2 8	A2 8	B2 8	B1 4.	

SING

Words & Music by Fran Healy

C#1 16	F#1 16	F#1 8	A1 4.	- 8	**TEMPO 80**
B1 4	C#2 32	B1 32	A1 8	B1 8	- 2	- 4	A1 16	B1 4.
- 8	F#2 8	E2 8	C#2 8	B1 8	C#2 32	B1 32	A1 4.	- 8
- 16	E1 16	E1 16	E1 16	G#1 8	A1 4.	- 16	B1 4	- 8
B1 8	A1 16	B1 4.	- 4	- 8	E1 16	F#1 16	A1 8	B1 4.
- 8	F#2 8	E2 8	C#2 8	B1 8	C#2 32	B1 32	A1 2	

STAYIN' ALIVE

Words & Music by Barry Gibb, Robin Gibb & Maurice Gibb

D#2 16	F2 16	- 16	G#2 16	- 16		TEMPO 125
- 16	D#2 8	- 8	C2 8	A#1 16	C2 16	D#2 8	A#1 16	C2 16
- 16	D#2 16	- 16	- 16	A#1 8	C2 8	D#2 8	F2 8	G#2 8
D#2 16	F2 16	- 16	G#2 16	- 8	D#2 8	- 8	C2 8	A#1 16
C2 16	D#2 8	A#1 16	C2 16	- 16	D#2 16	- 8	A#1 8	C2 8
D#2 8	F2 8	G#2 8				

SUMMER HOLIDAY

Words & Music by Bruce Welch & Brian Bennett

B1 4	B2 4	A2 8.	G#2 16	F#2 8.		TEMPO 125
E2 16	- 4	F#2 8.	G#2 16	F#2 8.	E2 16	C#2 4	- 4	B1 8.
B2 16	A2 8.	G#2 16	F#2 8.	E2 8	- 8	F#2 8.	G#2 16	F#2 2
B1 4	B2 4	A2 8.	G#2 16	F#2 8.	E2 16	- 4	F#2 8.	G#2 16
F#2 8.	E2 16	C#2 4	F#2 8.	F#2 16	G#2 16	F#2 8.	E2 16	C#2 4
E2 4	G#2 4	B1 2	F#2 8.	G#2 16	F#2 8.	E2 16	C#2 4	E2 2

STOP THE CAVALRY

Words & Music by Jona Lewie

D2 16	C2 16	B1 16	A1 16	G1 8			TEMPO 112
G1 8	D2 16	C2 16	B1 16	A1 16	G1 8	A1 16	B1 16	C2 8
D2 8	E2 16	F2 16	E2 8	E2 16	F2 16	E2 16	D2 16	E2 8
- 8	E2 16	F2 16	E2 16	D2 16	E2 2	D2 4	D2 8	C2 2
D3 8	D3 8	D3 16	E3 16	F3 8	F3 8	E3 8	E3 4	D3 8
D3 8	D3 16	E3 16	F3 8	F3 8	E3 8	C3 2

SUNSHINE OF YOUR LOVE

Words & Music by Jack Bruce, Pete Brown & Eric Clapton

D2 8	D2 8	C2 8	D2 8	- 8			TEMPO 125
A1 8	- 8	G#1 8	- 8	G1 8	- 8	D1 8	F1 4	D1 8
- 8	D2 8	D2 8	C2 8	D2 8	- 8	A1 8	- 8	G#1 8
- 8	G1 8	- 8	D1 8	F1 4	D1 8	- 8	G2 8	G2 8
F2 8	G2 8	- 8	D2 8	- 8	C#2 8	- 8	C2 8	- 8
G1 8	A#1 4	G1 8

TAINTED LOVE

Words & Music by Ed Cobb

G#1 4	G#1 4	B1 4	B1 4	E2 4
E2 4	B1 8	C#2 4.	G#1 4	G#1 4
B1 4	B1 4	E2 4	E2 4	B1 8
C#2 4	B1 8	G#1 4	G#1 4	B1 4
B1 4	E2 4	E2 4	B1 8	C#2 4
B1 8	G#1 2			

TEMPO 125

TAKE ON ME

Words & Music by Morten Harket, Mags Furuholmen & Pal Waaktaar

F#2 8	F#2 8	D2 8	B1 4	B1 4			
E2 4	E2 4	E2 8	G#2 8	G#2 8	A2 8	B2 8	A2 8
A2 8	E2 4	D2 4	F#2 4	F#2 4	F#2 8	E2 8	E2 8
E2 8	F#2 8	F#2 8	D2 8	B1 4	B1 4	E2 4	E2 8
G#2 8	G#2 8	A2 8	B2 8	A2 8	A2 8	A2 8	F#2 4
F#2 4	F#2 4	F#2 8	E2 8	E2 8	E2 4		

TEMPO 160

TAKE A CHANCE ON ME
Words & Music by Benny Andersson & Björn Ulvaeus

B1 16	C#2 16	D#2 8	F#2 4	B2 4.		TEMPO 112
- 8	B2 16	A#2 16	G#2 8	F#2 4	D#2 4.	- 8	B1 16	C#2 16
D#2 8	F#2 4	F#2 4.	- 8	B1 16	C#2 16	D#2 8	F#2 4	F#2 4.
- 8	C#2 16	D#2 16	E2 8	F#2 8	- 8	A#2 4	A#2 8	A#2 8
C#2 16	D#2 16	E2 8	F#2 4	F#2 4.	- 8	C#2 16	D#2 16	E2 8
F#2 8	- 8	A#2 4	A#2 8	A#2 8	C#2 16	D#2 16	E2 8	D#2 2

TELSTAR
By Joe Meek

A#2 2.	F2 4	G2 2.	F2 4	D#3 4		TEMPO 160
D3 4	C3 4	A#2 4	C3 4	F2 2.	D#3 4	D3 4	C3 4	A#2 4
C3 2	F2 2	F3 1.	F3 4	G3 2	F3 4	A#2 4	F3 2	D#3 2
D3 2	F#2 4	G2 4	D3 2	C3 2	D3 2.	D3 4	D#3 4	D3 4
C3 4	A#2 4	C3 2.	G2 8	A#2 8	A#2 4	A2 4	G2 4	F2 4
A#2 1						

THERE MUST BE AN ANGEL (PLAYING WITH MY HEART)

Words & Music by Annie Lennox & David A. Stewart

G1 8	A1 8	E2 8	D2 8	C2 8		**TEMPO 125**
B1 8	G1 2	A1 4.	D2 8	B1 2	B1 4.	E2 8	D2 16.
C2 16	A1 16	C2 4.	- 2	G1 8
A1 8	E2 8	D2 8	C2 8	B1 8
G1 8	A1 2	D2 4.	B1 8	B1 2
D2 4.	C2 8	C2 2.	A1 8.	C2 4

THE TIDE IS HIGH

Words & Music by John Holt, Howard Barrett & Tyrone Evans

G1 8	C2 4	C2 4	C2 4	C2 8		**TEMPO 112**
C2 8	A1 4.	C2 8	B1 2	C2 4	C2 8	A1 8	C2 4	C2 4
A1 4.	C2 8	B1 2	- 16	G2 4	E2 8	D2 16	C2 8	D2 8
E2 4	F2 8	D2 8	C2 4	B1 8	C2 4	D2 4	D2 4	E2 2
- 8	G2 8	F2 4.	E2 16	F2 16	G2 4.

THERE SHE GOES
Words & Music by Lee Mavers

| D2 8 | G2 8 | D2 8 | A2 8 | D2 8 | | TEMPO 140 |

| F#2 8 | D2 8 | G2 8 | D2 8 | E2 8 | D2 8 | E2 8 | D2 8 | E2 8 |

| D2 8 | G1 8 | D2 8 | G2 8 | D2 8 | A2 8 | D2 8 | F#2 8 | D2 8 |

| G2 8 | D2 8 | E2 8 | D2 8 | E2 8 | D2 8 | E2 8 | D2 8 | G1 8 |

| D2 8 | E2 8 | G2 8 | E2 8 | A2 4 | G2 8 | E2 8 | D2 8 | E2 8 |

| G2 8 | E2 8 | D2 8 | G2 8 | D2 8 | G2 8 | G2 8 | - 8 | A2 4 |

TROUBLE
Words & Music by Guy Berryman, Jon Buckland, Will Champion & Chris Martin

| F#2 16 | G2 16 | F#2 16 | D2 16 | B1 8. | | TEMPO 70 |

| B1 16 | F#2 16 | G2 16 | F#2 16 | D2 16 | B1 8. |

| B1 16 | F#2 16 | G2 16 | F#2 16 | D2 16 | B1 2 |

| B1 16 | A2 16 | G2 16 | F#2 16 | D2 16 | B1 8. |

| B1 16 | F#2 16 | G2 16 | F#2 16 | D2 16 | B1 8. |

| B1 16 | F#2 16 | G2 16 | F#2 16 | D2 16 | B1 2 |

TURN ON, TUNE IN, COP OUT
Words & Music by Norman Cook

D#1 4	- 8	D#1 8	F#1 8	A#1 4				TEMPO 125
G#1 4.	- 16	A#1 8	C#2 8	A#1 8	C#2 8	D#2 8	D#1 4	- 8
D#1 8	F#1 8	A#1 4	G#1 4.	- 16	A#1 8	C#2 8	A#1 8	C#2 8
D#2 8	D#1 4	- 8	D#1 8	F#1 8	A#1 4	G#1 4.	- 16	A#1 8
C#2 8	A#1 8	C#2 8	D#2 8	D#2 8	- 8	D#1 8	F#1 8	A#1 4
G#1 4.	- 16	A#1 8	C#2 8	A#1 8	C#2 8	D#2 8		

WALK OF LIFE
Words & Music by Mark Knopfler

B1 4.	B1 4.	- 4	- 8	F#1 8		TEMPO 180
G#1 8	B1 4	G#1 8	F#1 4	E1 4.	E1 4.
- 1	F#1 8	G#1 8	B1 4.	B1 4.	- 4
- 8	F#1 8	G#1 8	B1 4	G#1 8	F#1 4
E1 4.	E1 4.	- 4	- 8	F#1 8	G#1 8
B1 4	G#1 8	F#1 8	E1 4		

VOULEZ-VOUS
Words & Music by Benny Andersson & Björn Ulvaeus

E2 16	F2 16	E2 16	F2 16	E2 8			TEMPO 125
C2 4	A#1 8	F1 16	G1 16	A#1 16	C2 16	F1 16	G1 16	A#1 16
C2 16	F1 8	E1 8	C1 8	C#1 4	C1 8	E2 16	F2 16	E2 16
F2 16	E2 8	C2 4	A#1 8	F1 16	G1 16	A#1 16	C2 16	F1 16
G1 16	A#1 16	C2 16	F1 8	D#1 8	C1 8	C#1 8	C1 4	

WALK THIS WAY
Words & Music by Joe Perry & Steven Tyler

A1 16	A#1 16	B1 16	E2 16	- 16			TEMPO 112
A1 16	A#1 16	B1 16	E2 8	E1 8	- 4	A1 16	A#1 16	B1 16
E2 16	- 16	A1 16	A#2 16	B1 16	E2 8	G1 16	E1 16	E2 8
- 8	A1 16	A#1 16	B1 16	E2 16	- 16	A1 16	A#1 16	B1 16
E2 8	E1 8	- 4	A1 16	A#1 16	B1 16	E2 16	- 16	A1 16
A#1 16	B1 16	E2 8					

WHEELS
By Norman Petty

A1 4.	F1 8	C2 4.	A1 8	F2 8				TEMPO 180
A1 8	E2 8	A1 8	D2 8	C2 8	A1 8	F1 8	A#1 4.	E1 8
C2 4.	E1 8	E2 8	E1 8	D2 8	E1 8	C2 8	A#1 8	D1 8
E1 8	A1 4.	F1 8	C2 4.	A1 8	F2 8	A1 8	E2 8	A1 8
D2 8	C2 8	A1 8	F1 8	A#1 8	E1 8	G1 8	A#1 8	D2 8
C2 8	D1 8	E1 8	F1 2.					

A WHITER SHADE OF PALE
Words by Keith Reid
Music by Gary Brooker

E2 1	- 8	D2 8	C2 8	B1 8				TEMPO 112
C2 8	D2 8	E2 8	C2 8	A2 2.	B2 8	C3 8	F2 16	E2 16
F2 2	- 4	D2 4	B2 2.	C3 8	D3 16	G2 16	F2 16	G2 2
F2 8	E2 8	F2 8	F2 8	E2 8	D2 8	C2 8	C2 8	D2 8
E2 8	F2 8	B1 8	C2 8	D2 8	E2 8	F2 8	E2 8	F2 8
D2 8								

A FISTFUL OF DOLLARS

By Ennio Morricone

A1 8	D2 4	E2 8	F2 8	G2 8			TEMPO 140
F2 8	E2 8	D2 8	C2 4	A1 8	C2 8	D2 4.	A1 8	D2 4
E2 8	F2 8	G2 8	F2 8	E2 8	D2 8	C2 4	A1 8	C2 8
A1 4.	A1 8	D2 8	E2 8	F2 8	G2 8	F2 8	E2 8	D2 8
E2 4	F2 8	G2 8	A2 2.	C3 8	A2 8	A2 8	F2 2	D3 8
A2 8	A2 8	F2 4	D2 8	G2 2.	D2 8	E2 8	F2 1	D2 2

THE ADDAMS FAMILY

By Vic Mizzy

F1 8.	G1 8.	A1 8.	A#1 4.	G3 32			TEMPO 200
- 32	- 8	- 4	G3 32	- 32	- 8	- 4	G1 8.	A1 8.
B1 8.	C2 4.	G3 32	- 32	- 8	- 4	G3 32	- 32	- 8
- 4	G1 8.	A1 8.	B1 8.	C2 4.	G1 8.	A1 8.	B1 8.	C2 4.
F1 8.	G1 8.	A1 8.	A#1 4.	G3 32	- 32	- 8	- 4	G3 32

THE ARCHERS THEME
(BARWICK GREEN, EXCERPT FROM "MY NATIVE HEATH")
By Arthur Wood

C2 8.	A1 16.	F2 8.	D2 16.	C2 8.				TEMPO 125
A1 16.	F1 4	C2 8.	A1 16.	F2 8.	E2 4	D2 4	C2 8.	C2 8.
A1 16.	F2 8.	D2 16.	C2 8.	A1 16.	F1 4	G1 8.	C2 16.	B1 16.
C2 16	D2 16.	C2 2	D2 8.	E2 16.	F2 16.	E2 16	D2 16.	A#1 8.
C2 16.	D2 16.	C2 16	A#1 16.	A1 8.	A#1 16.	C2 16.	A#1 16	A1 16.
G1 2	C2 8.	A1 16.	F2 8.	D2 16.	C2 8.	A1 16.	F2 2	

AXEL F
(FROM THE FILM "BEVERLY HILLS COP")
By Harold Faltermeyer

F2 8	- 8	G#2 8.	F2 8	F2 16	TEMPO 125
A#2 8	F2 8	D#2 8	F2 8	- 8	
C3 8.	F2 8	F2 16	C#3 8	C3 8	
G#2 8	F2 8	C3 8	F3 8	F2 16	
D#2 8	D#2 16	C2 8	G2 8	F2 4.	

THE 'A' T...

By Mike Post & Pete ...

D#2 8.	D#2 16	A#1 8	D#2 2	- 8			TEMPO 140
G#1 8	A#1 4	D#1 4:	- 8	G1 32	A#1 32	B1 32	C#2 32	D#2 8
A#1 8	F2 8	D#2 2	- 8	C#2 8.	C2 16	A#1 16	G#1 8.	A#1 2
D#2 8.	D#2 16	A#1 8	D#2 2	- 8	G1 8	G#1 8	F1 8	A#1 8
D#1 2	G#1 8	G1 4	D#1 8	G#1 4	G1 4	G#1 4	A#1 4	C2 8
D2 4.	D#2 2						

BABY ELEPHANT WALK
(FROM THE FILM "HATARI!")
By Henry Mancini

F2 8.	A2 16	C3 8	F3 8	A3 8			TEMPO 140
G3 8	F3 8	D3 8	B2 8	C3 8	- 4	- 2	F2 8.	A2 16
C3 8	F3 8	A3 8	G3 8	F3 8	D3 8	B2 4	- 2	- 8
C3 8	G3 4	G3 4	D#3 32	E3 8	C3 8	- 8	C3 8	F3 4
F3 4	D#3 16	F3 16	D#3 16	C3 16	A#2 8	G#2 8	B2 4	B2 4
A#2 16	B2 16	A#2 16	G#2 16	F2 8	C2 8	D#2 8	F2 8	

DRAG RACER
(BBC SNOOKER THEME)
By Doug Wood

A1 4	G1 16	A1 8	A1 8.	A1 16	TEMPO 112
A1 8	A1 4	G1 8.	- 32	D2 8.	- 32	A1 2	E2 8.	E2 16
E2 16	D#2 16	D2 16	C2 8	B1 16	A1 16	G1 4	F1 8.	- 32
A#1 8.	- 32	E1 4	E1 16	F#1 16	A1 16	B1 16	A1 16	G1 16
A1 8	C2 16	C#2 16	E2 16	F#2 16	G#2 16	A2 8	A2 16	B2 32
C3 8	B2 16	A2 16	F#2 8	G2 8.	- 32	F#2 8.	- 32	E2 4

BIG BROTHER (UK TV THEME)
By Paul Oakenfold & Andy Gray

C2 16	C2 8	C2 16	C2 8	B1 16	TEMPO 160
B1 8	B1 16	B1 8	D2 16	D2 16	D2 8	C2 16	C2 8	C2 16
C2 8	D2 16	D2 8	D2 16	D2 8	D#2 16	D#2 16	D#2 8	E2 16
E2 8	E2 16	E2 8	E2 16	E2 8	E2 16	E2 8	E2 8	E2 8
E2 16	E2 8	E2 16	E2 8	E2 16	E2 8	E2 16	E2 8	E2 8
E2 8								

THE BANANA SPLITS THEME
(THE TRA-LA-LA SONG)
Words & Music by Ritchie Adams & Mark Barkan

A2 4	F#2 4	E2 4	- 8	A2 4		TEMPO 180
A2 8	F#2 4	E2 4	- 4	A2 4	F#2 4	E2 4	- 8	C#2 4
C#2 8	B1 4	A1 4	- 4	A2 4	F#2 4	E2 4	- 8	A2 4
A2 8	F#2 4	E2 4	- 4	A2 4	F#2 4	E2 4	- 8	C#2 4
C#2 8	B1 4	A1 4

BLACKADDER
By Howard Goodall

G1 4.	D1 8	G1 8	D1 8	G1 8		TEMPO 140
B1 8	C#2 2	- 4	A1 8	C2 4.	A1 8	C2 8	B1 8	A1 8
G1 8	G1 2	F#1 4.	D1 8	G1 4.	D1 8	G1 8	D1 8	G1 8
B1 8	C#2 4.	A1 8	C2 8	B1 8	A1 8	G1 8	G1 4.	A1 16
G1 16	F#1 8	- 4	D2 4	D2 2	B1 4	D2 4	D2 2	A1 4
D2 4	C2 2	D2 2	E2 2	F#2 2	G2 1

BLUE PETER THEME
(BARNACLE BILL)
By H. Ashworth-Hope

C1 16	D1 16	F1 8	F1 8	F1 16			TEMPO 112
G1 16	A1 16	A#1 16	C2 8	C2 8	C2 8	D2 16	E2 16	F2 16
G2 16	F2 16	D2 16	C2 8	D2 16	C2 16	A1 16	G1 16	F1 16
D1 16	F1 16	G1 8	C1 16	D1 16	F1 8	F1 8	F1 16	G1 16
A1 16	A#1 16	C2 8	C2 8	C2 8	F2 16	D2 16	E2 16	G2 16
E2 16	C2 16	A1 16	D2 16	B1 16	G1 16	C2 8	B1 8	C2 8

BULLITT
By Lalo Schifrin

G1 8	- 8	G2 8	- 8	G1 8			TEMPO 125
- 16	F#2 8	G1 16	F2 8	G1 8	- 8	E2 8	- 8	G1 8
- 16	F2 8	G1 16	F#2 8	G1 8	- 8	G2 8	- 8	G1 8
- 16	F#2 8	G1 16	F2 8	G1 8	- 8	E2 8	- 8	G1 8
D1 8	G1 8	A#1 8	A#1 32	C2 4	A#1 8	C2 8.	C2 16	A#1 8
C2 2							

THE BRIDGE ON THE RIVER KWAI
THEME (COLONEL BOGEY)
By Kenneth J. Alford

F2 8	D2 8	- 4	- 8	D2 8		TEMPO 140
D#2 8	F2 8	D3 8	- 8	D3 8	- 8	A#2 4.	- 8	F2 8
D2 8	- 4	- 8	D2 8	D#2 8	D2 8	F2 8	- 8	F2 8
- 8	D#2 4.	- 8	D#2 8	C2 8	- 4		C2 8	D2 8
D#2 8	F2 8	D2 8	- 4	- 8	D2 8	E2 8	D2 8	C2 8
F2 4	D2 8	E2 8	C2 4	G2 8	F2 2			

CASUALTY
By Kenneth Freeman

A1 8	B1 8	C#2 8	D2 4.	F2 4.				TEMPO 140
E2 4.	G2 2	F2 8	E2 8	D2 8	A2 2	A#2 4.	G2 2.	C#2 8
D2 8	E2 8	G2 4.	A#2 4.	A2 4.	F2 8	A1 8	D2 8	E2 8
F2 4.	A2 4.	G2 4.	F2 2	E2 8	D2 8	C#2 8	D2 2	- 8
D2 8	F2 8	A2 8	G2 4.	F2 4.	E2 4	D2 1		

CHARIOTS OF FIRE
By Vangelis

C#1 8	F#1 16.	G#1 16.	A#1 16	G#1 4		TEMPO 80
F1 4	- 8	C#1 8	F#1 16.	G#1 16.	A#1 16	G#1 2	- 8	C#1 8
F#1 16.	G#1 16.	A#1 16	G#1 4	F1 4	- 8	F1 8	F#1 16.	F1 16.
C#1 16	C#1 2	- 8	C#2 8	C2 16.	A#1 16.	G#1 16	C2 8.	G#1 16
A#1 8.	F#1 16	G#1 8.	C#2 16	C2 16.	A#1 16.	G#1 16	C2 2	- 8
F1 8	F#1 16.	F1 16.	C#1 16	C#1 2

DALLAS
By Jerrold Immel

G1 8	C2 4.	G1 8	G2 4.	C2 8		TEMPO 125
E2 4	D2 8	E2 8	C2 4	G1 4	C2 4	A2 4	G2 4	E2 8
		F2 8	G2 2.	- 8	G1 8	C2 4
		A2 4	G2 4	E2 8	F2 8	G2 4
		D2 8	E2 8	C2 4	G1 4	C2 4
		E2 8	F2 8	D2 4.	C2 8	C2 2

CHEERS THEME
(WHERE EVERYBODY KNOWS YOUR NAME)

Words by Judy Hunt Angelo
Music by Gary Portnoy

D2 8	D2 8	C2 8	D2 8	D#2 16			TEMPO 90
F2 8.	F2 8	F2 8	F2 16	G2 8.	F2 16	D#2 8.	D2 8	D#2 8.
C2 16	A#1 2	- 2	F2 8	F2 16	G2 8.	F2 8	D#2 8	D2 16
D#2 4	C2 16	A#1 4	- 2	F2 16	F2 16	F2 16	F2 8.	D2 8
C2 16	A#1 16	A#1 16	A#1 16	C2 4	A#1 8	A#1 4.		

DYNASTY
By Bill Conti

C2 4	G1 16	G1 4.	- 8	C2 4			TEMPO 125
G2 4	C2 16	C2 4.	- 8	C2 4	C3 8	B2 8	A2 4	G2 4
C2 16	C2 8.	D2 8	E2 8	F2 4	E2 8			
D2 8	C2 4	G2 4	A2 2	G2 8	F2 8			
G2 4	A2 2	G2 8	F2 8	C3 4	G2 2			
F2 8	E2 8	C2 4	D2 2					

EASTENDERS
By Leslie Osborne & Simon May

C2 8	D2 8	E2 8	F2 8	G2 4		TEMPO 100	
A2 4	F2 2	F2 8	E2 8	D2 8	C2 8	C2 4.	G1 8	G1 8.
C2 8.	G2 8	C2 8	D2 4.	G1 4.			
B1 8	C2 2	D2 4.	G2 8	C2 4.			
G2 8	G2 4.	F2 8	F2 4.	E2 8			
E2 8.	F2 8.	G2 8	E2 4	D2 4			

THE EXORCIST THEME
(TUBULAR BELLS)
By Mike Oldfield

E1 8	A1 8	E1 8	B1 8	E1 8		TEMPO 160	
G1 8	A1 8	E1 8	C2 8	E1 8	D2 8	E1 8	B1 8	C2 8
E1 8	A1 8	E1 8	B1 8	E1 8	G1 8	A1 8	E1 8	C2 8
E1 8	D2 8	B1 8	C2 8	E1 8	B1 8	E1 8	A1 8	E1 8
B1 8	E1 8	G1 8	A1 8	E1 8	C2 8	E1 8	D2 8	E1 8
B1 8	C2 8	E1 8	B1 8	E1 8	A1 4			

E.T.: THE EXTRA-TERRESTRIAL THEME
By John Williams

G1 8	E1 8	B1 8	C2 8	G1 8	TEMPO 140
E1 8	B1 8	C2 8	G1 8	F1 8	B1 8	C2 8	E2 8	F2 8
G2 8	A2 8	C3 8	G3 8	F3 8	E3 8	D3 8	E3 8	C3 2
G2 1	A2 2	A3 2	G3 8	F#3 8	E3 8	F#3 8	D3 2	B3 1
D2 2	C3 2	B2 8	A2 8	G2 8	F2 8	D#2 2	C2 2.	C2 16
B1 16	C2 16	D2 16	D#2 2	C2 2	C2 4.	B1 8	B1 2.	

FATHER TED THEME
(SONGS OF LOVE)
By Neil Hannon

C2 4	- 8	C2 8	A1 16	G1 8	TEMPO 90
A1 4.	- 16	A1 8	G1 8	E1 8	G1 4	- 8	G1 8	E1 16
D1 8	E1 4.	- 16	- 4	C2 8	D2 8	D2 8	C2 8	A1 8
C2 4	C2 8	C2 8	A1 8	G1 8	A1 8	A1 8	A1 8	G1 8
D#1 8	G1 4.	- 4	C2 8	D2 4.	C2 4	A1 8	C2 4.	-
B1 8	C2 2							

(MEET THE) FLINTSTONES
Words & Music by William Hanna, Joseph Barbera & Hoyt Curtin

© Copyright 1960 Barbera-Hanna Music, USA.
EMI Music Publishing Limited, 127 Charing Cross Road, London, WC2.
All Rights Reserved. International Copyright Secured

C2 4	F1 8	- 4	F2 4	D2 8				TEMPO 200
C2 4	F1 8	- 4	C2 4	A#1 8	A1 8	A1 8	A#1 8	C2 8
F1 4	G1 4	A1 4	- 8	- 8	- 8	C2 4	F1 4	- 8
F2 4	D2 8	C2 4	F1 4	- 8	C2 4	A#1 8	A1 8	A1 8
A#1 8	C2 8	F1 4	G1 4	- 16	A1 8	A#1 8	C2 8	F1 4
G1 4	- 8	A1 8	A#1 8	C2 8	F2 4	G2 4	F2 2	

THE GOOD, THE BAD AND THE UGLY
By Ennio Morricone

© Copyright 1966 Alberto Grimaldi Productions, Italy. EMI United Partnership Limited,
print rights controlled by Warner Bros. Publications Incorporated/IMP Limited.
Used by permission. All Rights Reserved. International Copyright Secured

A2 16	D3 16	A2 16	D3 16	A2 2				TEMPO 125
F1 4	G1 4	D1 2.	A2 16	D3 16	A2 16	D3 16	A2 2	F1 4
G1 4	C2 2.	A2 16	D3 16	A2 16	D3 16	A2 2	F1 4	E1 8
D1 8	C1 2.	A2 16	D3 16	A2 16	D3 16	A2 4.	G1 4	D1 8
D1 2								

THE GODFATHER (LOVE THEME)

By Nino Rota

G1 8	C2 8	D#2 8	D2 8	C2 8			TEMPO 100
D#2 8	C2 8	C#2 32	D2 8	C2 8	G#1 8	A#1 8	G1 2	- 8
G1 8	C2 8	D#2 8	D2 8	C2 8	D#2 8	C2 8	C#2 32	D2 8
C2 8	G1 8	F#1 8	F1 2	- 8	F2 8	G#2 8	B2 8	D3 2
- 8	F2 8	G#2 8	B2 8	C3 2	- 8	C1 8	D#1 8	A#1 8
G#1 8	G1 8	A#1 8	G#1 8	G#1 8	G1 8	G1 8	B1 8	C2 2

GRANGE HILL

By Alan Hawkshaw

A2 8	B2 8.	E2 32	F2 4	D2 2			TEMPO 140
- 2	A1 8	C#2 16	D2 8.	F2 8	F#2 16	D3 8.	A2 8	B2 16
F2 8	F#2 16	D2 8.	C2 8.	D2 8.	D2 8.	F2 8	F#2 16	A2 4
- 8	C2 4.	C#2 8.	A1 8	C#2 16	D2 8.	F2 8	F#2 16	D3 8.
A2 8	B2 16	F2 8	F#2 16	D2 8.	C2 8.	D2 8.	D2 8.	F2 8
F#2 16	A2 8.	A2 16.	C3 8.	A2 16	G2 8	F2 16	G2 8	F2 2

THE GREAT ESCAPE

By Elmer Bernstein

A#1 8	D#2 8	- 4	A#1 8	G2 8.		TEMPO 112
F2 16	D#2 8	C2 8	- 2	- 8	F2 8	F2 4	D#2 8	D2 8.
D#2 16	D2 8	C2 8	A#1 8	G1 8	- 4	- 8	G1 8	G#1 8
A1 8	A#1 8	D#2 8	- 4	- 8	A#1 8	G2 8.	F2 16	D#2 8
C2 8	- 8	- 2	F2 8	F2 4	D#2 8	D2 8	A#1 4	F2 8
D#2 2

HAPPY DAYS

Words by Norman Gimbel
Music by Charles Fox

C1 4	F1 4	A1 4	C2 4	D2 8		TEMPO 180
E2 4	D2 4.	- 4	D1 4	G1 4	A#1 4	D2 4	E2 8	F2 4
E2 4.	- 4	E1 4	A1 4	C#2 4	E2 4
F2 8	G2 4	F2 4.	- 4	D2 8	D2 4
E2 4.	- 4	D2 8	D2 4	E2 4.	- 4
E2 8	E2 8	E2 4	F2 4	F#2 8	G2 2

GROUND FORCE

By Jim Parker

F2 8	F2 8	A#1 16	A#1 16	A#1 8		TEMPO 140
F2 16	F2 16	F2 8	A#1 16	A#1 16	A#1 8	F1 8	A#1 4	F#1 2
A#1 4	F1 4	A#1 4	D2 4	F2 4	C2 2.	F2 16	F2 16	F2 8
A#1 16	A#1 16	A#1 8	F2 16	F2 8	F1 8	A#1 16	A#1 16	A#1 8
F2 8	F#2 2	C#2 2	F#2 4	F2 8	F1 16	F1 16	F1 8	F1 8
C2 8	F1 16	F1 16	F1 8	F1 8	A#1 2		

I DREAM OF JEANNIE

By Hugo Montenegro

G1 4	D2 8	- 16	- 8	D2 16.		TEMPO 140
- 16	C2 16.	- 16	E2 16	D2 8.	C2 8	- 32	F1 4	D2 8
- 8	- 16	D2 16.	- 16	C2 16.	- 16	E2 16	D2 8.	C2 8
- 32	G1 4	D2 8	- 16	- 8	D2 16.	- 16	C2 16.	- 16
E2 16	D2 8.	C2 8	- 32	F2 8.	- 4	C2 16	D#2 8	- 16
E2 8	- 16	F2 8					

E THERE FOR YOU
("... THEME)

...usic by Michael Skloff, Allee Willis, Philip Solem,
..., Marta Kauffman & Danny Wilde

A2 8	C#3 8	C#3 16	B2 16	A2 16				TEMPO 112
G2 8	G2 8	A2 16	B2 8	A2 8	A1 8	C#2 8	C#2 16	B1 16
A1 16	G1 8	G1 8	A1 16	B1 8	A1 8	- 8	E2 8.	D2 8
C#2 8.	A1 8	C#2 16	B1 4.	- 8	B1 16	C#2 16	D2 8	C#2 8.
B1 8	B1 16	A1 8	- 16	E2 8.	D2 8	C#2 8.	A1 8	C#2 16
B1 4.	- 16	B1 16	C#2 16	D2 8	C#2 8.	B1 8	B1 2.	A1 1

THE ITALIAN JOB THEME:
GETTA BLOOMIN' MOVE ON! (THE SELF PRESERVATION SOCIETY)
By Quincy Jones

E1 8	F#1 8	E1 4	G#1 8.	TEMPO 125
E1 16	F#1 8	E1 4	C#1 8	E1 4
F#1 8	E1 4	E1 8	F#1 8	E1 8
G#1 4	G#1 8.	E1 16	F#1 8	E1 4
C#1 8	E1 4	F#1 8	E1 4	

FILM & TV THEMES

INSPECTOR GADGET
Words & Music by Haim Saban & Shuki Levy

D1 8	E1 8	F1 8	G1 8	A1 4		TEMPO 225
F1 4	G#1 4	E1 4	G1 4	F1 4	D1 8	E1 8	F1 8	G1 8
A1 4	D2 4	C#2 4	C#3 8	- 8	C#3 8	- 8	- 4	D1 8
E1 8	F1 8	G1 4	A1 4	F1 4	G#1 4	E1 4	G1 4	F1 4
D1 4	- 2	G1 16	A1 16	B1 16	C#2 16	D2 4

THE JAMES BOND THEME
By Monty Norman

B1 2	C2 2	C#2 2	C2 2	B1 2		TEMPO 140
C2 2	C#2 2	C2 2	E1 8	F#1 16	F#1 16	F#1 8	F#1 4	E1 8
E1 8	E1 8	E1 8	G1 16	G1 16	G1 8	G1 4	F#1 8	F#1 8
F#1 8	E1 8	F#1 16	F#1 16	F#1 8	F#1 4	E1 8	E1 8	E1 8
E1 8	G1 16	G1 16	G1 8	G1 4	F#1 8	F1 8	E1 8	D2 8
C#2 2	- 16	A1 8	G1 8	A1 2

JUNGLE BOOGIE
(FROM THE FILM "PULP FICTION")

Words & Music by Ronald Bell, Robert Bell, Claydes Smith, George Brown, Dennis Thomas, Robert Mickens, Donald Boyce & Richard Westfield

G1 8	G1 16	A#1 8	A#1 16	F1 8.	**TEMPO 100**
G1 8.	A#1 8.	C2 8.	C#2 8.	D2 8.	F2 4	F#2 4	A#2 8	A#2 16
G2 8	G2 16	A2 8.	A#2 8.	G2 8.	F#2 8.	F2 8.	D2 8.	C#2 4
C2 8.	G2 8	G2 16	A#2 8	A#2 16	F2 8.	G2 8.	A#2 8.	C3 8.
C#3 8.	D3 8.	F3 4	F#3 4	A#3 8	A#3 16	G3 8	G3 16	A3 8.
A#3 8.	G3 8.	F#3 8.	F3 8.	D3 8.	C#3 4	C3 4

KNIGHT RIDER

By Stu Phillips & Glen Larson

F#1 8	C#2 16	B1 16	C#2 2	- 4	**TEMPO 125**
F#2 8	G2 16	F#2 16	C#2 2	- 4	F#1 8	C#2 16	B1 16	C#2 8
F#2 8	E2 2	- 2	F#1 8	C#2 16	B1 16	C#2 2	- 4	F#2 8
G2 16	F#2 16	C#2 2	- 4	F#1 8	C#2 16	B1 16	C#2 8	F#2 8
G2 2

JURASSIC PARK

By John Williams

A#1 16	A1 16	A#1 4.	A#1 16	A1 16		TEMPO 90
A#1 4.	A#1 16	A1 16	A#1 8.	C2 16	C2 8.	D#2 16	D#2 4.	D2 16
A#1 16	C2 8.	A1 16	F1 8	D2 16	A#1 16	C2 4.	F2 16	A#1 16
D#2 8.	D2 16	D2 8.	C2 16	C2 16	A#2 16	A2 16	A#2 16	F2 16
D#2 8	A#2 16	A2 16	A#2 8	F2 8	D#2 8	A#2 16	A2 16	A#2 4
F2 8	A#1 8	A#2 4	A2 8	A#2 16	A2 16	A#2 2	F3 2	A#3 2

LITTLE GREEN BAG
(FROM THE FILM "RESERVOIR DOGS")

Words & Music by Jan Visser & James Bouwens

G1 8	- 8	F1 8	G1 8	A#1 8		TEMPO 112
G1 8	F1 8	G1 8	G1 8	F1 8	C1 8	D1 4.	- 4	D1 8
- 8	C1 8	D1 8	F1 8	D1 8	C1 8	D1 8	F1 8	G1 8
A#1 8	G1 4.	F1 8	G1 4	F1 16	G1 8	D1 16	A#1 16	G1 8
D1 16	F1 16	G1 4	C1 8	C#1 8	D1 2	D1 8	- 8	C1 16
D1 8	D1 16	F1 16	D1 8	C1 16	C1 16	D1 4	F1 8	G1 2

LIVE AND LET DIE
Words & Music by Paul & Linda McCartney

G2 16	A2 16	A#2 8	- 8	D2 16		TEMPO 100
E2 16	F2 4	C2 16	A#1 16	G1 8	G2 16	A2 16	A#2 8.	D2 16
E2 16	F2 8	C2 8	A#1 4	G2 16	A2 16	A#2 8	- 8	D2 16
E2 16	F2 4	C2 16	A#1 16	G1 8	G2 16	A2 16	A#2 8.	D2 16
E2 16	F2 8	C2 8	A#1 4

THE MAGIC ROUNDABOUT
By Alain Legrand, Jacques Charriere, Serge Danot & Luc Aulivier

A2 4	A2 8	A2 8	E2 4	E2 4		TEMPO 140
F#2 8	F#2 8	F#2 8	F#2 8	D2 4	D2 4	G2 4	G2 8	G2 8
D2 4	D2 4	G#2 4	G#2 4	E2 2	A2 4	A2 8	A2 8	E2 4
E2 4	F#2 8	F#2 8	F#2 8	F#2 8	D2 4	D2 4	G2 4	G2 8
G2 8	D2 4	D2 4	G#2 4	G#2 4	E2 2

LOVE IS ALL AROUND
(FROM THE FILM "FOUR WEDDINGS AND A FUNERAL")
Words & Music by Reg Presley

F2 8	D3 8	D3 8	C3 8	A#2 8			TEMPO 112
C3 8	G2 2	D#3 8	D#3 8	D3 8	C3 8	C3 4	D3 2	- 2
F2 8	D3 8	D3 8	C3 8	A#2 8	C3 2	G2 2	D#3 8	D#3 8
D3 8	C3 8	C3 4	D3 4	- 4	F3 8	F3 8	D3 16	F3 8
D3 16	G3 8	F3 4.	- 2	A#2 8	A2 8	A#2 8	C3 8	D3 8
A#2 4.	F3 2.	A#2 8	A2 8	A#2 8	C3 8	D3 8	A#2 2

MISSION: IMPOSSIBLE
By Lalo Schifrin

G1 4.	G1 4.	A#1 4	C2 4	G1 4.			TEMPO 180
G1 4.	F1 4	F#1 4	G1 4.	G1 4.	A#1 4	C2 4	G1 4.	G1 4.
F1 4	F#1 4	A#2 16.	G2 16.	D2 1	A#2 16.	G2 16.	C#2 1	A#2 16.
G2 16.	C2 1	A#1 8	C2 8	- 2	A#2 16.	G2 16.	F#2 1
A#2 16.	G2 16.	F2 1	A#2 16.	G2 16.	E2 1	D#2 8	D2 8

THE MONKEES
Words & Music by Tommy Boyce & Bobby Hart

C1 8.	D1 8	E1 2.	- 8	E1 8				TEMPO 125
D1 16	E1 8	G1 8.	A1 2.	- 8	A1 16	A1 8.	A1 8	G1 16
F1 8.	A1 4	A1 2	G1 16	A1 8	D2 4	D2 2	B1 2	-
E2 8	E2 8	D2 16	C2 8	E2 4	E2 2	G1 16	C2 8.	C2 8
C2 16	D2 8	C2 16	D2 8	E2 2	- 8	G1 16	C2 8.	C2 8.
D2 8	D2 8.	E2 8.	C2 2	G1 16	C2 8.	C2 8.	D2 4.	A1 2

THE MUNSTERS
By Jack Marshall

D2 4	D2 4	D2 4	C2 4	B1 8				TEMPO 125
C2 8	A1 8	B1 8	G1 4	- 4	A1 4	A1 4	A1 4	G1 4
F#1 8	G1 8	E1 8	F#1 8	D#1 4	- 4	B2 8	B2 8	F#2 8
G2 8	B2 8	B2 8	F#2 8	G2 8	C3 8	C3 8	G#2 8	A2 8
C3 8	C3 8	G2 8	A2 8	B2 8	B2 8	F#2 8	G2 8	B2 8
B2 8	F#2 8	G2 8	G2 8	G2 8	D2 8	E2 8	E1 4	D1 8

MONTY PYTHON'S FLYING CIRCUS
THEME (LIBERTY BELL MARCH)
By John Philip Sousa

A#1 16	G1 8	G1 16	G1 16	F#1 16			TEMPO 100
G1 16	D#2 8	A#1 16	A#1 8	G1 16	G#1 8	G#1 16	G#1 8	A#1 16
C2 4	- 16	G#1 16	F1 8	E1 16	F1 16	E1 16	F1 16	D2 8
C2 16	C2 8	G#1 16	G1 8	G1 16	G1 8	G#1 16	A#1 4	- 16
A#1 16	G1 8	G1 16	G1 16	F#1 16	G1 16	G2 8	D#2 16	D#2 8
A#1 16	C2 8	F2 16	F2 16	F2 16	F2 4			

THE PINK PANTHER THEME
By Henry Mancini

G#1 8	A1 2	B1 8	C2 2	G#1 8			TEMPO 140
A1 8.	B1 8	C2 8.	F2 8	E2 8.	A1 8	C2 8.	E2 8	D#2 2
D2 16	C2 8	A1 16	G1 8	A1 1	A2 8.	G2 8	E2 8.	D2 8
C2 8.	A1 8	D#2 16	D2 4	D#2 16	D2 4	D#2 16	D2 4	D#2 16
D2 4	C2 8	A1 8	G1 8	G1 16	A1 8.	G1 16	A1 8.	G1 16
E1 8								

PANTHER PINK PANTHER FROM HEAD TO TOES

Words & Music by Doug Goodwin

C#2 8.	C#2 16	B1 8.	C#2 4	E2 4				TEMPO 140
B1 8	C#2 8.	C#2 16	B1 8.	C#2 4	E2 4	- 4	A1 8
B1 8	C#2 8.	E2 8.	B2 2.	A2 8	F#2 8	G#2 8	A2 4	A2 4
A2 4	A2 4	A2 8	G#2 8	A2 8	F#2 4	E2 8	D2 4	C#3 8
B2 8	A2 8	C#3 4	B2 8	A2 8	F#2 8	A2 2	B2 2	A2 2

POSTMAN PAT

Words & Music by Bryan Daly

E2 8	G2 8	A2 8	- 8	E2 8				TEMPO 100
G2 8	A2 8	- 8	E2 8	G2 8	A2 8	C3 16	C3 16	B2 16
B2 16	G2 8	A2 4.	- 4	F2 8	G2 8	A2 8	F2 8	E2 8.
D2 8.	- 8	F2 8	G2 8	A2 8	F2 8	E2 8.	D2 8.	- 8
F2 8	G2 8	A2 8	F2 8	E2 8	D2 8	C2 16	B1 8.	C2 2

I'M POPEYE THE SAILOR MAN

Words & Music by Sammy Lerner

G1 8.	A#1 8	A#1 8	A#1 8	G#1 8.	TEMPO 160
G1 8	A#1 2	A#1 8	C2 8	G#1 8	C2 8	D#2 8.	C2 8	A#1 2
A#1 8	C2 8	G#1 8	C2 8	D#2 8	D2 8	C2 8	A#1 8	C2 8
A#1 8	G1 8	D#1 8	G1 8	A#1 8	A#1 8	A#1 8	C2 4	D2 8
D#2 4	A#2 32	C3 32	D3 32	D#3 16

RAIDERS OF THE LOST ARK THEME
(RAIDERS MARCH)
By John Williams

E1 8.	F1 16	G1 8	C2 2	C2 8	TEMPO 125
D1 8.	E1 16	F1 2.	G1 8.	A1 16	B1 8	F2 2	F2 8	A1 8.
B1 16	C2 4	D2 4	E2 4	E1 8.	F1 16	G1 8	C2 2	C2 8
D2 8.	E2 16	F2 2.	G1 8.	G1 16	E2 4	D2 8.	G1 16	E2 4
D2 8.	G1 16	E2 4	D2 8.	G1 16	F2 4	E2 8.	D2 16	C2 4

RANDALL AND HOPKIRK (DECEASED)
By Edwin Astley

C#1 4	F#2 2	A1 4	C#2 4	D2 2.	TEMPO 125
A1 4	G#1 32	A1 32	G#1 32	F#1 32	G#1 4.	D#2 4	E2 4	C#2 2.
C#1 4	D1 2	F#1 4	E1 4	D#1 32	E1 32	D#1 32	C#1 32	D#1 2
- 8	D#1 4	D1 2	G1 4	D1 4	C#1 2.	C#1 4	F#1 2	A1 4
C#2 4	D2 2.	A1 4	G#1 32	A1 32	G#1 32	F#1 32	G#1 4.	D#2 4
E2 4	C#3 8	E2 8	G#2 8	C#3 8	E3 8	G#3 4.

SCOOBY DOO, WHERE ARE YOU?
Words & Music by Ben Raleigh & David Mook

C#2 8	C#2 8	B1 8	B1 8	A1 2	TEMPO 160

B1 8	C#2 4	F#1 2	F#1 8	G#1 4	E1 4	C#2 4	B1 8	B1 4

		A1 2	- 4	C#2 8	C#2 8	B1 4
B1 8	A1 2	B1 8	C#2 4	D2 2
B1 8	E1 4	E1 4	C#2 4	B1 8
B1 4	A1 2

RED DWARF
By Howard Goodall

E1 4	G1 4	B1 2	C2 16	B1 16		TEMPO 125
C2 16	E2 16	B1 2	E1 4	G1 4	B1 2.	A1 16	G1 16	E2 2
- 4	E2 4	F#2 4.	G2 4.	F#2 8	G2 8	F#2 8	E2 8	F#2 8
G2 2	D2 2	F2 2	E2 1	A1 2	D#2 2	D2 1	D2 2	F2 2
E2 1	A1 2	D#2 2	D2 1

SHAKESPEARE IN LOVE THEME
(THE BEGINNING OF THE PARTNERSHIP)
By Stephen Warbeck

F2 4.	D#2 8	D2 4	F2 4	C2 2		TEMPO 80
C2 4.	D2 16	D#2 16	F2 4.	D#2 8	D2 4	F2 4	C2 4.	A#1 8
A1 8	D2 4	D#2 16	F2 16	G2 2.	F2 8	D#2 8	D2 8	G2 8
C2 2.	A1 16	A1 16	A#1 16	A#1 16	C2 16	C2 16	D#2 16	D#2 16
F2 4.	D#2 8	D2 4	F2 4	C2 2	C2 4.	D2 16	D#2 16	F2 4.
D#2 8	D2 4	F2 4.	C2 8	A#1 8	A1 8	D2 4	D#2 4	D2 2.

THE SIMPSONS

By Danny Elfman

| C2 4. | E2 4 | F#2 4 | A2 8 | G2 4. | | TEMPO 160 |

| E2 4 | C2 4 | A1 8 | F#1 8 | F#1 8 | F#1 8 | G1 2 | - 4 | F#1 8 |

| | | | | F#1 8 | F#1 8 | G1 8 | A#1 4 |

| | | | | - 8 | C2 8 | C2 8 | C2 8 |

| | | | | C2 4 |

STAR TREK:
THE MOTION PICTURE THEME

By Jerry Goldsmith

| G1 2 | F2 2. | E2 4 | D2 8. | C2 8 | | | | TEMPO 140 |

| B1 8. | A#1 2 | A#1 1. | G1 2 | G2 2. | F2 4 | E2 8. | D2 8 | C2 8. |

| B1 2 | B1 1 | A#1 4 | A1 4 | B1 4 | C#2 4 | D2 4 | E2 8. | F#2 8 |

| G2 8. | A2 2 | A#2 1. | A#1 2. | C2 4 | D2 4 | D#2 4 | F2 8. | G2 8 |

| G#2 8. | A#2 2 | B2 1. |

SKI SUNDAY THEME
(POP LOOKS BACH)
By Sam Fonteyn

A2 8	G2 8	A2 8	F#2 8	A2 8				TEMPO 180
E2 8	A2 8	D2 8	A2 8	C#2 8	A2 8	D2 8	A2 8	E2 8
A2 8	F#2 8	A1 8	D2 8	C#2 8	B1 8	D2 8	A1 8	D2 8
G1 8	D2 8	F#1 8	D2 8	G1 8	D2 8	A1 8	D2 8	B1 8
D2 8	G2 8	F#2 8	E2 8	G2 8	D2 8	G2 8	C#2 8	G2 8
B1 8	G2 8	C#2 8	G2 8	D2 8	G2 8	E2 4.	D2 8	D2 2

THE SWEENEY
By Harry South

C1 16	G#1 8.	F1 2.	C1 16	C2 8.				TEMPO 140
A#1 2.	- 2	G#1 8	G#1 8.	F1 16	G#1 8.	C2 4.	A#1 8.	F1 16
G#1 4	A#1 8	- 16	C1 16	G#1 8.
F1 2.	C1 16	C2 8.	A#1 2.	- 2
C2 16	C2 8.	B1 16	C2 8.	D2 2
G1 8	G#1 4	G1 2

TFI FRIDAY THEME
(MAN IN A SUITCASE)
By Ron Grainer

C1 8	D#1 4	G1 2	- 4	C1 8			TEMPO 180
D#1 16.	G1 8	- 8	F1 4.	C1 8	D#1 4	G1 2	- 8	C1 8
D#1 16.	G1 8	- 8	F1 4.	C1 8	D#1 4	G1 1	- 8	G#1 8.
G1 16	G1 8.	G1 16	G1 8.	G1 16	G1 8.	G1 16	G1 8.	G1 16
G1 8.	G1 16	F#1 8.	G1 16	- 8	C2 2	- 8	B1 4	- 4
A#1 4	- 8	G1 8	A#1 8	B1 8	- 8	C2 2		

TOP CAT
Words & Music by William Hanna, Joseph Barbera & Hoyt Curtin

A#1 8	A#1 4	- 2	G1 16	A#1 8			TEMPO 125
G1 16	A1 8	G1 16	F1 8	A#1 8.	A#1 4	- 2	A#1 16	A#1 8
G1 16	A1 8	G1 16	F1 8	- 16	A#1 8.	A#1 8.	A#1 8.	A#1 8.
G1 8	G#1 16	A1 8	A#1 4	- 8	C2 8.	C2 8.	C2 8.	C2 8.
C2 16.	A1 16.	G1 16.	F1 4					

THUNDERBIRDS
By Barry Gray

G#2 8	D#2 16	G#2 16	A#2 4.	D#2 16	TEMPO 125
F2 16	G#2 8	A#2 8	D#3 8	F3 16	
C#3 16	D#3 8	F3 8	A#2 2	G#2 8	
D#2 16	G#2 16	A#2 4.	D#2 16	F2 16	
G#2 8	A#2 8	D#3 8	F3 16	C3 16	
D#3 8	F3 8	G3 2			

THE WIZARD
("TOP OF THE POPS" THEME FROM 1986-1991)
By Paul Hardcastle

G1 8	F1 16	G1 16	A#1 16	G1 8			TEMPO 125
- 8	G1 8	F1 16	G1 16	A#1 16	G1 8	- 8	G1 8	F1 16
G1 16	A#1 16	G1 8	- 8	A#1 4	A1 4	G1 8	F1 16	G1 16
A#1 8	C2 16	A#1 16	C2 16	C#2 16	C2 16	A#1 8	- 4	- 8
F1 16	F#1 16	G1 8	F1 16	F#1 16	G1 8	A#1 8	C2 16	D2 16
F2 16	G2 2							

THE X FILES
By Mark Snow

A1 16	C2 16	E2 16	F2 16	A1 16		TEMPO 100
C2 16	F2 16	A1 16	C2 16	E2 16	- 4	A1 8.	E2 8.	D2 8.
E2 8.	G2 8.	E2 2	- 8	- 4	A1 8.	E2 8.	D2 8.	E2 8.
A2 8.	E2 2	- 8	- 4	C3 8.	B2 8.	A2 8.	G2 8.	A2 8.
E2 2	- 4	- 8	C3 8.	B2 8.	A2 8.	G2 8.	B2 8.	E2 2

YOU ONLY LIVE TWICE
By John Barry

C#2 8	C2 16	C#2 16	C2 8	A#1 16		TEMPO 90
C2 16	A#1 4	G#1 4	B1 8	A#1 16	B1 16
A#1 8	G#1 16	A#1 16	G#1 4	F#1 4	C#2 8
C2 16	C#2 16	C2 8	A#1 16	C2 16	A#1 4
G#1 4	B1 8	A#1 16	B1 16	A#1 8	G#1 16
A#1 16	G#1 4	F#1 4

A NIGHT IN TUNISIA
By Frank Paparelli & Dizzy Gillespie

A#1 16	C#2 16	F2 16	C3 4	A#2 8.			TEMPO 100
F2 16	G#2 8	A2 4.	- 4	- 8	A1 16	A#1 16	C#2 16	F2 4
C3 8	C3 4.	A#2 8	F2 8	A2 8	- 8	A1 8	A#1 8	C#2 8
F2 8	C3 8	A#2 8	F2 8	G#2 8	A2 4.	- 2	A2 8	A#2 8
A2 16	A#2 16	A2 16	G2 8	D#2 4	C#2 8	D2 4.		

BARCAROLLE
By Jacques Offenbach

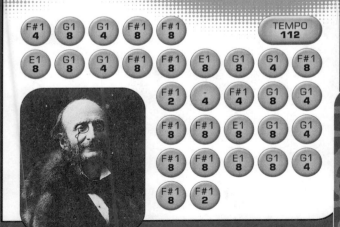

F#1 4	G1 8	G1 4	F#1 8	F#1 8			TEMPO 112
E1 8	G1 8	G1 4	F#1 8	F#1 8	E1 8	G1 8	G1 4	F#1 8
			F#1 2	- 4	F#1 4	G1 8	G1 4
			F#1 8	F#1 8	E1 8	G1 8	G1 4
			F#1 8	F#1 8	E1 8	G1 8	G1 4
			F#1 8	F#1 2			

ANTHROPOLOGY
By Dizzy Gillespie & Charlie Parker

TEMPO 140

F1 8	A#1 8	D2 8	C2 8	A#1 8				
D#2 8	C#2 8	D2 8	F2 8	- 4	-	D#2 8	- 8	F2 8
D#2 4	-	D2 8	D#2 8	D2 8	C2 8	A1 8	A#1 8	D2 8
C2 8	G1 8	A#1 8	A1 8	- 4	-	A#1 4.	G1 8	A#1 8
D2 8	A#1 8	- 8	E2 4	D#2 4	F#1 4	A#1 8	C2 8	D2 8
F2 4	- 8	A#1 8	-	G#2 4	F#2 8	G2 2	D2 8	F2 8

THE BARBER OF SEVILLE
By Gioacchino Rossini

TEMPO 160

B2 8	B2 8	C3 8	B2 8	- 2				
B2 8	B2 8	C3 8	B2 2	B2 8	B2 8	B2 8	C3 8	B2 4
A2 8	A2 8	G2 4	F#2 8	F#2 8	E2 8	E2 4.	G2 8	G2 8
G2 8	G2 32	F#2 8	E2 4	G2 8	G2 32	F#2 8	E2 4	G2 8
B2 8	F#2 8	F#2 4.	F#2 8	G2 8	A2 8	A2 8	G2 8	G2 16
F#2 16	E2 8	E2 16	D2 16	C2 8	C2 16	B1 16	A#1 8	B1 2

THE ARRIVAL OF THE QUEEN OF SHEBA
By George Frideric Handel

							TEMPO
A#2 16	F2 16	D2 16	F2 16	A#2 16			112
F2 16	D2 16	F2 16	C2 16	A#2 16	A2 16	G2 16	F2 16	D#2 16
D2 16	C2 16	D2 16	A#1 16	C2 16	D2 16	D#2 16	F2 16	G2 16
A2 16	A#2 16	F2 16	D2 16	F2 16	A#2 16	F2 16	D2 16	F2 16
A#2 16	E2 16	C2 16	E2 16	A#2 16	G2 16	C2 16	G2 16	A2 16
G2 16	F2 16	G2 16	C2 8	E2 8	F2 8

THE BLUE DANUBE
By Johann Strauss

							TEMPO
C2 4	E2 4	G2 4	G2 4	- 4			180
G3 4	G3 4	- 4	E3 4	E3 4	- 4	C2 2	E2 4	G2 2
- 4	G3 4	G3 4	- 4	F3 4	F3 4	- 4	B1 2	D2 2
A2 4	A2 4	- 4	A3 4	A3 4	- 4	F3 4	F3 4	- 4
D1 4	F1 4	A1 4	A1 1	F#1 4	G1 4	E2 1	C2 4	E1 4
E1 2	D1 4	A1 2	G1 4	C2 8	- 8	C2 8	C2 4	C2 4

THE CAN CAN
By Jacques Offenbach

D2 2	E2 8	G2 8	F#2 8	E2 8	TEMPO 180

A2 4	A2 4	A2 8	B2 8	F#2 8	G2 8	E2 4	E2 4	E2 8
G2 8	F#2 8	E2 8	D2 8	D3 8	C#3 8	B2 8	A2 8	G2 8
F#2 8	E2 8	D2 2	E2 8	G2 8	F#2 8	E2 8	A2 4	A2 4
A2 8	B2 8	F#2 8	G2 8	E2 4	E2 4	E2 8	G2 8	F#2 8
E2 8	D2 8	A2 8	E2 8	F#2 8	D2 8			

THEME FROM CELLO CONCERTO
Composed by Edward Elgar

E1 4	F#1 8	E1 4	G1 8	A1 4	TEMPO 90

G1 8	F#1 4	D1 8	C1 8	D1 8	B1 4	A1 8	G1 4	A1 8
G1 4	B1 8	C2 4	B1 8	A1 4	F#1 8	E1 4	F#1 8	D#1 4
B1 8	B2 4.	A2 4.	A#2 4.	B2 16	B1 16	C#1 16	D#1 16	E1 16
F#1 16	G1 16	A1 16	B1 16	C#2 16	D#2 16	E2 16	F#2 16	G2 16
A2 16	B2 16	C#3 16	D#3 16	E3 4				

CAPRICE

By Niccolò Paganini

A2 4.	A2 8	A2 8	A#2 8	A2 8				TEMPO 200
G2 8	F2 4.	D2 8	D2 8	F2 8	E2 8	D2 8	G2 4.	G2 8
G2 8	A2 8	G2 8	F2 8	E2 4.	C2 8	C2 8	E2 8	D2 8
C2 8	F2 4.	B1 8	B1 8	D2 8	C2 8	B1 8	E2 4.	A1 8
A1 8	C2 8	B1 8	A1 8	F1 4	- 8	D#1 8	E1 8	E2 8
D2 8	B1 8	A1 4	- 4	G2 32	A2 4			

CHANSON DE MATIN

Composed by Sir Edward Elgar

F2 4	F2 4	F2 8	E2 8	D2 8				TEMPO 125
E2 16	F2 16	C2 8	A#1 8	G1 2.	A1 32	A2 4	A2 4	A2 8
G2 8	F2 8	G2 16	A2 16	F2 8	E2 8	C2 2.	- 8	D2 16
E2 16	F2 8	E2 16	D2 16	G2 4	D2 4.	C2 16	D2 16	E2 8
D2 16	C2 16	F2 4	C2 4.	A#1 16	C2 16	D2 8	C2 16	A#1 16
E2 4	A#1 4	A1 4.	C2 32	A#1 8	A1 2			

DANCE OF THE SUGAR PLUM FAIRY
By Peter Ilyich Tchaikovsky

G3 16	E3 16	G3 8	F#3 8	D#3 8			TEMPO 100
E3 8	D3 16	D3 16	D3 8	C#3 16	C#3 16	C#3 8	C3 16	C3 16
C3 8	B2 16	E3 16	C3 16	E3 16	B2 16	- 4	G2 16	E2 16
G2 8	F#2 8	C3 8	B2 8	G3 16	G3 16	G3 8	F#3 16	F#3 16
F#3 8	E3 16	E3 16	E3 8	D3 16	D3 16	D3 8	C3 16	C3 16
C3 8	D#3 16	F#3 16	E3 16	F#3 16	D#3 8		

DOUBLE VIOLIN CONCERTO
By Johann Sebastian Bach

D1 16	E1 16	F1 16	G1 16	A1 8	TEMPO 90
D2 8	C#2 8	A1 8	E1 8	G1 8	F#1 8
D1 8	C2 4.	B1 16	A1 16	B1 8	G1 8
E1 8	G1 8	A#1 8	D1 8	C#1 8	A1 8
D1 8	G1 8	F1 4	F1 32	E1 32	F1 32
E1 32	F1 32	E1 8	D1 2		

DANCE OF THE SWAN
By Peter Ilyich Tchaikov[...]

G1 8	G1 8	G1 8	G1 8	F#1 16			TEMPO 125
G1 16	A1 8	G1 8	F#1 8	A1 8	A1 8	A1 8	A1 8	G1 16
A1 16	B1 8	A1 8	G1 8	B1 8	E2 8	D#2 8	B1 8	F#1 8
B1 16	A1 16	G1 16	F#1 16	E1 8	B1 8	E2 8	D#2 8	B1 8
F#1 8	B1 16	A1 16	G1 16	F#1 16	E1 8	- 8	E3 8

EINE KLEINE NACHTMUSIK
By Wolfgang Amadeus Mozart

G2 4.	D2 8	G2 4.	D2 8	G2 8			TEMPO 140
D2 8	G2 8	B2 8	D3 4	- 4	C3 4.	A2 8	C3 4.	A2 8
C3 8	A2 8	F#2 8	A2 8	D2 4	- 4	G2 4	G2 4.	B2 8
A2 8	G2 8	G2 8	F#2 8	F#2 4.	A2 8	C3 8	F#2 8	G2 8
G2 8	G2 16	F#2 16	E2 16	F#2 16	G2 8	G2 8	A2 8	A2 8
B2 8	B2 8	D3 16	C3 16	B2 16	C3 16	D3 4

D#1	E1	C2	E1				TEMPO
16	**16**	**8**	**16**				**100**

C2	E1	C2	C3	D3	D#3	E3	C3	D3
8	**16**	**4.**	**16**	**16**	**16**	**16**	**16**	**16**

E3	B2	D3	C3	C3	D3	E3	C3	D3
8	**16**	**8**	**4.**	**16**	**16**	**16**	**16**	**16**

E3	C3	D3	C3	E3	C3	D3	E3	C3
8	**16**	**16**	**16**	**16**	**16**	**16**	**8**	**16**

D3	C3	E3	C3	D3	E3	B2	D3	C3
16	**16**	**16**	**16**	**16**	**8**	**16**	**8**	**4.**

TROIKA (FROM LIEUTENANT KIJÉ)
By Sergey Prokofiev

A1	D2	C#2	B1	C#2			TEMPO
8	**8**	**8**	**8**	**8**			**140**

D2	B1	A1	B1	F#1	A1	B1	A1	G1
4	**4**	**4**	**4**	**4**	**4**	**8**	**8**	**4**

D2	C#2	D2	A1	G1	F#1	E1	B1	A1
4	**8**	**8**	**2.**	**8**	**8**	**8**	**4**	**4**

G1	A1	G1	F#1	G1	A1	D2	B1	G1
4	**8.**	**16**	**8.**	**16**	**4**	**8**	**8**	**4**

F#1	G1	A1	A1	D1				
8	**8**	**4**	**4**	**1**				

FEVER

Words & Music by John Davenport & Eddie Cooley

D2 8.	C2 16	D2 8.	C2 16	D2 8.			TEMPO 125
A1 4	C2 4	D2 4	- 2	D2 8.	C2 16	D2 8.	C2 16	D2 8.
C2 16	A1 8.	A1 4	- 2	- 4	D2 8.	C2 16	D2 8.	C2 16
D2 8.	A1 4	C2 4	D2 4	- 4	A1 16.	A1 8.	A1 16	D2 8.
C2 16	D2 8.	C2 16	D2 8.	C2 16	A1 8.	A1 4	A1 16	A1 8.
A1 16	C2 4	A1 4

FLOWER DUET

By Leo Delibes

B1 4.	A1 16	B1 16	C2 4	B1 4.			TEMPO 80
A1 16	B1 16	C2 4	B1 16	C2 16	B1 16	C2 16	D2 16	E2 16
D2 16	C2 16	B1 16	A1 16	G1 16	A1 16	G1 16	A1 16	G1 16
A1 16	F#1 2	B1 4.	A1 16	B1 16	C2 4	B1 16	C2 16	B1 16
C2 16	D2 16	E2 16	D2 16	C2 16	B1 16	A1 16	G1 16	A1 16
G1 16	A1 16	G1 16	A1 16	G1 8	B1 32	A1 8	G1 8	D2.

SPRING (FROM THE FOUR SEASONS)
By Antonio Vivaldi

D#2 8	G2 8	G2 8	G2 8	F2 16				TEMPO 125
D#2 16	A#2 4.	A#2 16	G#2 16	G2 8	G2 8	G2 8	F2 16	D#2 16
A#2 4.	A#2 16	G#2 16	G2 8	G#2 16	A#2 16	G#2 8	G2 8	F2 8
D2 8	A#1 8	G2 8	A#2 8	G#2 16	G2 16	G#2 8	A#2 8	C3 8
A#2 4	G2 8	A#2 8	G#2 16	G2 16	G#2 8	A#2 8	C3 8	A#2 4
G2 8	C3 8	A#2 4	G#2 8	G2 8	F2 16	D#2 16	F2 4	D#2 2

AIR ON THE G STRING
By Johann Sebastian Bach

F#2 8	D2 8	C#2 8	C#1 8	B1 8				TEMPO 50
B2 8	A2 8	A1 8	G1 8	B2 16	G2 16	F#2 32	E2 16	D2 16
C#2 16	D2 16	C#2 4	B1 16	A1 8.	A2 8	C2 16	B1 16	C2 8
A2 16	C2 16	B1 16	F#2 16	C2 16	B1 16	E2 16	D#2 16	A2 16
G2 16	G2 8	E2 16	D2 16	E2 16	F#2 16	G2 16	E2 16	A1 16
E2 16	B1 16	A1 16	D2 16	C#2 16	G2 16	F#2 16	F#2 4.	

JAZZ & CLASSICAL

FÜR...

By Ludwig V...

E2 8	D#2 8	E2 8	D#2 8	E2 8	**TEMPO 125**
B1 8	D2 8	C2 8	A1 4.	C1 8	E1 8	A1 8	B1 4.	E1 8
C2 8	B1 8	A1 4.	B1 8	C2 8	D2 8	E2 8	G1 8	F2 8
E2 8	D2 4.	F1 8	E2 8	D2 8	C2 4.	E1 8	E2 8	D#2 8
E2 8	D#2 8	E2 8	B1 8	D2 8	C2 8	A1 4.	C1 8	E1 8
A1 8	B1 4.	E1 8	C2 8	B1 8	A1 2

THE GIRL FROM IPANEMA

Music by Antonio Carlos Jobim
Original Words by Vinicius De Moraes
English Words by Norman Gimbel

G2 4.	E2 8	E2 4	D2 8	G2 4.	**TEMPO 140**
E2 8	E2 4	E2 8	D2 8	G2 4.	E2 4
E2 4	D2 8	G2 4	G2 8	E2 8	E2 4
E2 8	D2 8	F2 4	D2 8	D2 8	D2 4
C2 8	E2 4	C2 4	C2 4	C2 8	A#1 4
- 4	C2 2.

GREENSLEEVES

Traditional

A1 8	C2 4	D2 8	E2 8.	F#2 16			TEMPO 112
E2 8	D2 4	B1 8	G1 8.	A1 16	B1 8	C2 4	A1 8	A1 8.
G1 16	A1 8	B1 8	G1 8	E1 4	- 8	G2 4.	G2 8.	F#2 16
E2 8	D2 4	B1 8	G1 8.	A1 16	B1 8	C2 8.	B1 16	A1 8
G#1 8.	F#1 16	G#1 8	A1 4,	A1 4

HIT THE ROAD JACK

Words & Music by Percy Mayfield

G2 8.	D#2 16	F2 2	C2 4.	C2 8			TEMPO 160
D#2 8.	D#2 16	F2 4	F2 4	D#2 4	G2 4	G2 4	C3 4	C3 4
D#3 4	D#3 4	C3 4	G2 4	D#2 16	F2 2	C2 4.	C2 8	D#2 8.
D#2 16	F2 4	F2 4	C2 4	C2 1	D#2 8.	D#2 16	F2 4	F2 4
C2 4	C2 1	D#2 8.	D#2 16	F2 4	F2 4	C2 4	C2 1

HABANERA (FROM CARMEN)

By Georges Bizet

D2 8	C#2 8	C2 16.	C2 16	C2 16.			TEMPO 80
B1 8	A#1 8	A1 8	A1 16	A1 16	G#1 8	G1 8	F1 16. · G1 32
F1 32	E1 16	F1 16	G1 8	F1 8	E1 8	-	D2 8 · C#2 2
C2 16.	C2 16	C2 16.	B1 8	A#1 8	A1 16	A1 16	- 16 · A1 16
G1 8	F1 8	E1 16.	F1 32	E1 32	D1 16	E1 16	F1 8 · E1 8
D1 8							

HORNPIPE (TRUMPET TUNE)

By Henry Purcell

G2 4	G2 4	G2 4.	- 16	F2 16			TEMPO 140
E2 8.	D2 16	C2 8.	E2 16	D2 4	G1 4	E1 4	G1 4 · C2 4
G1 4	C2 8.	D2 16	E2 8.	F2 16	D2 2	G2 4	G2 4 · G2 4.
- 16	F2 16	E2 8.	D2 16	C2 8.	E2 16	D2 4	G1 4 · C2 8.
D2 16	C2 8.	D2 16	E2 8.	F#2 16	E2 8.	F#2 16	G2 32 · F#2 32
G2 32	F#2 32	G2 32	F#2 32	G2 32	F#2 4	E2 16	F#2 16 · G2 4

HORNPIPE
(FROM THE WATER MUSIC)
By George Frideric Handel

G1 2	C2 2	D2 2	E4 4	C2 2		TEMPO 225
D2 4	E2 4	C2 4	D2 4	G2 2	D2 4	E2 4	D2 8	C2 8
D2 4	G2 4	D2 4	E2 4	D2 8	C2 4	D2 4	G1 2	G2 2
G2 4	G2 4	G2 4	F2 8	E2 8	F2 8	F2 4	F2 4	F2 4
F2 4	E2 4	D2 8	E2 8	G2 8	F2 8	G2 8	E2 8	G2 8
F2 8	G2 2.	G1 4	G1 2.	C2 4	F2 2	E2 2	D2 2	C2 1

JESU JOY OF MAN'S DESIRING
By Johann Sebastian Bach

G2 8	A2 8	B2 8	D3 8	C3 8		TEMPO 125
C3 8	E3 8	D3 8	D3 8	G3 8	F#3 8	G3 8	D3 8	B2 8
G2 8	A2 8	B2 8	C3 8	D3 8	E3 8	C3 8	C3 8	B2 8
A2 8	B2 8	G2 8	F#2 8	G2 8	A2 8	D2 8	F#2 8	A2 8
C3 8	B2 8	A2 8	B2 8	G2 8	A2 8	B2 8	D3 8	C3 8
C3 8	E3 8	D3 8	D3 8	G3 8	F#3 8	G3 4

IN THE HALL OF THE MOUNTAIN KING

By Edvard Grieg

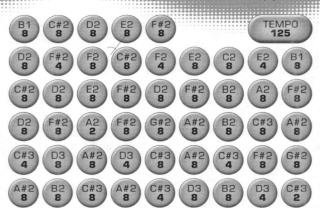

B1 8	C#2 8	D2 8	E2 8	F#2 8				TEMPO 125
D2 8	F#2 4	F2 8	C#2 8	F2 4	E2 8	C2 8	E2 4	B1 8
C#2 8	D2 8	E2 8	F#2 8	D2 8	F#2 8	B2 8	A2 8	F#2 8
D2 8	F#2 8	A2 2	F#2 8	G#2 8	A#2 8	B2 8	C#3 8	A#2 8
C#3 4	D3 8	A#2 8	D3 4	C#3 8	A#2 8	C#3 4	F#2 8	G#2 8
A#2 8	B2 8	C#3 8	A#2 4	C#3 8	D3 8	B2 8	D3 4	C#3 2

'JUPITER'
(FROM THE PLANETS SUITE)

Composed by Gustav Holst

G1 8	A#1 8	C2 4.	D#2 8	D2 8.				TEMPO 90
A#1 16	D#2 8	F2 8	D#2 4	D2 4	C2 8	D2 8	C2 4	A#1 4
G1 2	G1 8	A#1 8	C2 4.	D#2 8	D2 8.	A#1 16	D#2 8	F2 8
G2 4	G2 4	G2 8	F2 8	D#2 4	F2 4	D#2 2	G2 8	A#2 8
C3 4.	D#3 8	D3 8.	A#2 16	D#3 8	F3 8	G3 4	G3 4	G3 4
F3 4	D#3 2	F3 2	D#3 2					

CARO NOME

By Giuseppe Verdi

G2 8.	F#2 16	E2 4	D2 4	C2 4			TEMPO 125
B1 4	A1 2	- 4	F#2 8.	E2 16	D2 4	C2 4	B1 4	A1 4
G1 2	- 4	B2 8.	A2 16	G2 16	A2 16	G2 8	F#2 16	G2 16
F#2 8	E2 16	F#2 16	E2 8	D2 16	E2 16	D2 8	A1 2.	F#2 8.
E2 16	E2 16	D2 16	B2 16	D2 16	D2 16	C2 16	A2 16	C2 16
C2 16	B1 16	G2 16	B1 16	B1 16	A1 16	E2 16	D2 16	G1 2.

LULLABY OF BIRDLAND

Words by George David Weiss
Music by George Shearing

B2 8.	B2 16	A2 8.	G2 16	F#2 8			TEMPO 125
E2 4.	C#2 4	E2 8	D#2 2	- 8	B1 4	F#2 8	E2 2	- 8
C2 4	B2 8	A2 2	- 8	D3 8.	D3 16	C3 8.	B2 16	A2 8
G2 4.	E2 8	B2 8	A2 8	D#2 4	B2 8	A2 8	D2 2.	A2 8
G2 8	C2 4	G2 8	F#2 8	B1 2			

JAZZ & CLASSICAL

LA DONNA E MOBILE

By Giuseppe Verdi

B2 4	B2 4	B2 4	B2 32	D3 8.				TEMPO 160
C3 16	A2 2	A2 4	A2 4	A2 4	A2 32	C3 8.	B2 16	G2 2
B2 4	A2 4	G2 4	A2 32	G2 8.	F#2 16	F#2 2	A2 4	G2 4
E2 4	F#2 32	E2 8.	D2 16	D2 2	D3 8.	C3 16	D3 4	D3 4
E3 2	D3 2	D#3 2	- 4	F#3 8.	E3 16	D3 8.	C3 16	B2 8.
A2 16	G2 4	G3 4						

MAPLE LEAF RAG

By Scott Joplin

G#1 16	D#2 16	G#1 16	C2 16	D#2 8				TEMPO 112
G1 16	D#2 16	G1 16	A#1 16	D#2 4	- 8	G#1 16	D#2 16	G#1 16
C2 16	D#2 8	G1 16	D#2 16	G1 16	A#1 16	D#2 8.	- 16	D#2 16
- 16	G#1 16	B1 16	E2 16	- 16	D#2 16	- 16	D#2 16	- 16
G#1 16	B1 16	E2 16	- 16	D#2 16	- 16	G#1 16	B1 16	G#2 8
G#2 16	B2 16	G#3 8	G#2 16	B2 16	G#3 8	G#3 16	B3 16	G#3 16

MINUET
By Luigi Boccherini

G2 **32**	A2 **32**	G2 **16**	F#2 **16**	G2 **16**		TEMPO **125**
A2 **16**	G2 **8**	G1 **4**	B1 **4**	D2 **8**	D2 **8**	C2 **8**	C2 **4**	C2 **32**
D2 **32**	C2 **16**	B1 **16**	C2 **16**	D2 **16**	C2 **8**	D1 **4**	A1 **8**	C2 **8**
C2 **8**	B1 **8**	B1 **4**	G2 **8.**	E2 **16**	D2 **8**	C#2 **8**	C#2 **8**	C#2 **8**
G2 **8.**	E2 **16**	D2 **8**	C#2 **8**	C#2 **8**	C#2 **8**	G2 **8.**	E2 **16**	F#2 **8**
D2 **8**	B1 **8**	G2 **8**	F#2 **32**	G2 **32**	E2 **4**	D2 **32**	E2 **32**	D2 **4**

POMP AND CIRCUMSTANCE
MARCH NO. 1 (LAND OF HOPE AND GLORY)
By Sir Edward Elgar

G2 **2**	F#2 **8**	G2 **8**	A2 **4**	E2 **2**	TEMPO **160**
D2 **2**	C2 **2**	B1 **8**	C2 **8**	D2 **4**	A1 **1**
B1 **2**	C#2 **8**	D2 **4**	E2 **8**	A2 **2**	D2 **2**
C3 **2**	C3 **8**	D2 **4**	A2 **8**	B2 **1**	E2 **2**
F#2 **8**	G2 **4**	A2 **8**	D2 **2**	G2 **2**	G1 **2**
C2 **8**	B1 **4**	A1 **8**	G1 **1**		

'MORNING' (FROM PEER GYNT)

By Edvard Grieg

G2 8	F2 32	E2 8	D2 8	C2 8			TEMPO 90
D2 8	E2 8	G2 8	F2 32	E2 8	D2 8	C2 16	D2 16	E2 16
D2 16	E2 16	G2 8	E2 8	G2 8	A2 8	E2 8	A2 8	G2 8
E2 8	D2 8	C2 4	– 8	G1 8	F1 32	E1 8	D1 8	C1 8
D1 8	E1 8	G1 8	F1 32	E1 8	D1 8	C1 8	D1 16	E1 16
D1 16	E1 16	G1 8	E1 8	G1 8	A1 8	E1 8	A1 8	B1 2

NEW WORLD SYMPHONY THEME (HOVIS ADVERT)

By Antonin Dvořák

E1 8.	G1 16	G1 4	E1 8.	D1 16			TEMPO 90
C1 4	D1 8.	E1 16	G1 8.	E1 16	D1 2	E1 8.	G1 16	G1 4
E1 8.	D1 16	C1 4	D1 8.	E1 16	D1 8.	C1 16	C1 2	A1 8.
C2 16	C2 4	B1 8	G1 8	A1 4	A1 8	C2 8	B1 8	G1 8
A1 2	E1 8.	G1 16	G1 4	C2 8.	D2 16	E2 4	D2 8.	C2 16
D2 8	A1 8	C2 2	D2 4.	C2 8	D2 4	A1 4	C2 2

ODE TO JOY
By Ludwig Van Beethoven

E2-2, F2-4, G2-2, F2-4, E2-4 | TEMPO 180

D2-4, C2-2, D2-4, E2-4, E2-4., D2-8, D2-2, E2-2, F2-4

G2-2, F2-4, E2-4, D2-4, C2-2, D2-4, E2-4, D2-4., C2-8

C2-2, D2-2, E2-4, C2-4, D2-4, E2-8, F2-8, E2-4, C2-4

D2-4, E2-8, F2-8, E2-4, D2-4, C2-4, D2-4, G1-4, E2-2.

F2-4, G2-2, F2-4, E2-4, D2-4, C2-2., E2-4, D2-2, C2-2

PICTURES AT AN EXHIBITION
By Modest Mussorgsky

A1-4, G1-4, C2-4, D2-8, G2-8 | TEMPO 125

E2-4, D2-8, G2-8, E2-4, C2-4, D2-4, A1-4, G1-4, A1-4

G1-4, C2-4, D2-8, G2-8, E2-4, D2-8, G2-8, E2-4, C2-4

D2-4, A1-4, G1-4, G1-4, A1-4, E1-4, G1-8, A1-4, D1-4

A1-8, B1-8, G1-4, G2-4, E2-4, D2-8, C2-8, G1-4, A1-4

G1-4, C2-4, D2-8, G2-8, E2-4, C2-4, F2-2, D2-2, C2-2

JAZZ & CLASSICAL

BRIDAL MARCH
By Richard Wagner

F1 4	A#1 8.	A#1 16	A#1 4.	- 8			TEMPO 140
F1 4	C2 8.	A1 16	A#1 4.	- 8	F1 4	A#1 8.	D#2 16	D#2 4
D2 8.	C2 16	A1 8	C2 16	A#1 16	A1 16	A#1 16	C2 8	- 8
F1 4	A#1 8.	A#1 16	A#1 4.	- 8	F1 4	C2 8.	A1 16	A#1 4.
- 8	F1 4	A#1 8.	D2 16	F2 4	D2 8.	A#1 16	G1 4	C2 8.
D2 16	A#1 4.

HALLELUJAH CHORUS
(FROM THE MESSIAH)
By George Frideric Handel

D2 4.	A1 8	B1 8	A1 8	- 4			TEMPO 125
D2 4.	A1 8	B1 8	A1 8	- 8	D2 16	D2 16	D2 8	D2 8
- 8	D2 16	D2 16	D2 8	D2 8	- 8	D2 8	C#2 8	D2 8
C#2 8	D2 4	- 4	E2 4.	A1 8	F#2 8	E2 8	- 4	E2 4.
A1 8	F#2 8	E2 8	- 8	E2 16	E2 16	F#2 8	E2 8	- 8
E2 16	E2 16	F#2 8	E2 4	E2 8	F#2 8	E2 8	D2 4	C#2 4

JAZZ & CLASSICAL

117

'PIZZICATI' (FROM SYLVIA)

By Leo Delibes

A#1 16	F1 16	G#1 16	D#1 16	G1 16		TEMPO 100
A#1 16	C2 16	D#2 16	D2 8	F2 8	A#2 8.	C2 16	D#2 16	A#1 16
D2 16	G#1 16	C2 16	D2 16	F2 16	G#2 16	G2 8	A#2 8	D#3 8.
A#1 16	D#2 16	A#1 16	C#2 16	C2 16	F2 16	C2 16	D#2 16	D2 16
G2 16	D2 16	F2 16	D2 16	D#2 16	F2 16	G2 16	G#2 16	A#2 16
G2 16	G#2 16	A2 16	A#2 16	B2 16	C3 16	D3 16	D#3 8	D#3 4

PRELUDE IN A MAJOR

By Frederik Chopin

E1 4	C#2 8.	D2 16	B1 4	B1 4		TEMPO 125
B1 2	F#2 4	D#2 8.	E2 16	A2 4	A2 4	A2 2	C#2 4	A#1 8.
B1 16	D2 4	D2 4	D2 2	G#1 4	G#1 8.	A1 16	C#2 4	C#2 4
C#2 2	E1 4	C#2 8.	D2 16	B1 4	B1 4	B1 2	F#2 4	D#2 8.
E2 16	C#3 4	C#3 4	C#3 2	C#2 4	C#2 8.	D2 16	F#2 4	F#2 4
F#2 4	G#1 4	B1 8.	A1 16	A1 32	A2 4	A2 4	A2 2	

POLICEMAN'S SONG
By Sir Arthur Sullivan

F1 8	G1 8	A1 8	C2 8	A#1 8				TEMPO 160
A1 8	G1 8	A#1 8	A1 8	G1 8	F1 8	E1 8	F1 8	A1 8
C1 8	C1 8	C1 8	C1 8	D1 8	C#1 8	D1 8	D1 8	D1 8
A1 8	G1 8	F1 8	E1 4	C1 8	C1 4	C1 8	F1 8	G1 8
A1 8	C2 8	A#1 8	A1 8	G1 8	A#1 8	A1 8	G1 8	F1 8
E1 8	F1 8	G1 8	C1 8	C1 8	C1 4	D1 2	G1 2	F1 2

PRELUDE IN C MINOR
By Johann Sebastian Bach

C2 16	D#2 16	G2 16	D#2 16	C2 16				TEMPO 112
D#2 16	C2 16	- 16	C2 16	- 16	C2 16	- 16	C2 16	F2 16
G#2 16	F2 16	C2 16	F2 16	C2 16	- 16	C2 16	- 16	C2 16
- 16	B1 16	D2 16	F2 16	D2 16	B1 16	D2 16	B1 16	- 16
B1 16	- 16	B1 16	- 16	G1 16	C2 16	D#2 16	C2 16	G1 16
C2 16	G1 16	- 16	G1 16	- 16	G1 16			

THE QUEEN OF THE NIGHT'S ARIA

By Wolfgang Amadeus Mozart

E2 **32**	D2 **16**	C2 **16**	D2 **16**	E2 **16**	TEMPO **160**
F2 **8**	F2 **8**	F2 **8**	C2 **8**	G2 **8**	G2 **8**	G2 **8**	C2 **8**	A2 **8**
F2 **8**	A2 **8**	C3 **8**	F3 **8**	C3 **8**	D3 **8**	A#2 **8**	C3 **8**	F2 **8**
A2 **8**	C3 **8**	F3 **8**	C3 **8**	D3 **8**	A#2 **8**	C3 **4**	- **4**	F2 **2**
G2 **4.**	G2 **8**	G#2 **4.**	G#2 **8**	A2 **2**	F2 **2**	C2 **2.**	D2 **8**	E2 **8**
F2 **2**

RONDO

By Wolfgang Amadeus Mozart

D2 **4**	C2 **16**	A1 **16**	G1 **8**	G1 **8**	TEMPO **160**
G1 **8**	E2 **4**	C2 **16**	A1 **16**	F#1 **8**	F#1 **8**	F#1 **8**	G1 **8**	D1 **8**
B1 **8**	A1 **8**	D1 **8**	C2 **8**	B1 **8**	D1 **8**	D2 **8**	B1 **4**	A1 **8**
D2 **4**	C2 **16**	A1 **16**	G1 **8**	G1 **8**	G1 **8**	E2 **4**	C2 **16**	A1 **16**
F#1 **8**	F#1 **8**	F#1 **8**	G1 **8**	B1 **8**	D2 **8**	E2 **8**	G2 **8**	C2 **8**
B1 **8**	C2 **8**	A1 **8**	G1 **4**

JAZZ & CLASSICAL

THE RIDE OF THE VALKYRIES
By Richard Wagner

B2 8	A1 16	B1 16	D2 4	B1 4			TEMPO 112
D2 8	B1 16	D2 16	F#2 4	D2 4	F#2 8	E2 16	F#2 16	A2 4
A1 4	D2 8	B1 16	D2 16	F#2 2	- 2	- 8	D2 8	D2 8
B1 16	D2 16	F#2 4	D2 4	F#2 8	E2 16	F#2 16	A2 4	F#2 4
A2 8	F#2 16	A2 16	C#3 4	C#2 4	F#2 8	E2 16	F#2 16	A#2 2

RULE BRITANNIA
By Thomas Arne

B1 4.	B1 8	C2 8	C2 8	- 8			TEMPO 125
B1 8	C2 8.	B1 16	A1 8	G1 8	F#1 2	D2 4	C2 4	B1 16
G1 16	C2 16	A1 16	D2 8	C2 8	B1 4	A1 4	G1 4.	- 8
B1 4.	B1 8	C2 8	C2 8	- 8	B1 8	C2 8.	B1 16	A1 8
G1 8	F#1 2	D2 4	C2 4	B1 16	G1 16	C2 16	A1 16	D2 8
C2 8	B1 4	A1 4	G1 4.					

SO WHAT
By Miles Davis

D1 16	A1 8.	B1 16	C2 8.	D2 16			TEMPO 140
E2 8.	C2 16	D2 8	A1 4.	B2 4.	A2 8	- 8	D1 16	A1 8.
B1 16	C2 8.	D2 16	E2 8.	C2 16	D2 2	B2 4.	A2 8	-
E2 4.	E2 4	E2 8	D2 4.	A1 4.	B2 4.	A2 8	- 8	D#1 16
A#1 8.	C2 16	C#2 8.	D#2 16	F2 8.	C#2 16	D#2 2	C3 4.	A#2 8
- 8	F2 4.	F2 4	F2 8	D#2 4.	A#1 4.	C3 4.	A#2 8	

SONATINA IN A MINOR
By Friedrich Kuhlau

G#2 32	A2 8	A1 8	A1 8	A1 8			TEMPO 112
A1 8.	C2 32	B2 32	A1 8	A1 8	A1 16	B1 16	C2 16	B1 16
A1 16	B1 16	C2 16	D2 16	E2 2	D#3 32	E3 8	E2 8	E2 8
E2 8	E2 8	G2 32	F2 32	E2 8	E2 8	E2 8	F2 16	G2 16
F2 16	E2 16	D2 16	C2 16	B1 16	A1 4.	G#2 32	A2 8	A1 4.
G#2 32	A2 8	A1 8.						

SOLFEGGIETTO
By Carl Philipp Emanuel Bach

F1 8	D1 8	F1 8	A1 8	D2 8			TEMPO 160
F2 8	E2 8	D2 8	C#2 8	A1 8	C#2 8	E2 8	A2 8	G2 8
F2 8	E2 8	F2 8	D2 8	F2 8	A2 8	D3 8	F3 8	E3 8
D3 8	E3 8	D3 8	C#3 8	B2 8	A2 8	G2 8	F2 8	E2 8
D2 4

MOMENT MUSICAL
By Franz Schubert

C2 32	A#1 8	A#1 16	C2 16	A#1 8			TEMPO 140
A1 8	A#1 32	C2 32	D2 4	A#1 32	C2 32	D2 4	C2 32	A#1 8
A#1 16	C2 16	A#1 8	D2 8	D2 32	G2 4	D2 32	G2 4	G#2 32
G2 8	G2 16	G#2 16	G2 8	G2 8	G2 8	C3 4	G2 8	D2 16
C2 16	A#1 16	C2 16	D2 16	D#2 16	D2 16	F#2 16	G2 4	G2 4

STRAIGHT NO CHASER
By Thelonious Monk

G1 16	C2 16.	D2 16	D#2 16.	E2 8			TEMPO 100
G1 16	C2 16.	D2 16	D#2 16.	E2 16	F2 16.	D#2 4.	- 8	G1 16
C2 16.	D2 16	D#2 16.	E2 8	G1 16	C2 16.	D2 16	D#2 16.	E2 4
G1 16	C2 16.	D2 16	D#2 4	- 8	G1 16	C2 16.	D2 16	D#2 16.
E2 16	F2 16.	D#2 2	- 8	G1 16	C2 16.	D2 16	D#2 16.	E2 8
G1 16	C2 16.	D2 16	D#2 16.	E2 4.	G1 16	C2 16.	D2 16	D#2 2

SYMPHONY NO. 5 THEME
By Ludwig Van Beethoven

G1 8	G1 8	G1 8	D#1 2	- 8			TEMPO 200
F1 8	F1 8	F1 8	D1 1	- 8	G1 8	G1 8	G1 8	D#1 8
G#1 8	G#1 8	G#1 8	G1 8	D#2 8	D#2 8	D#2 8	C2 2	-
G1 8	G1 8	G1 8	D1 8	G#1 8	G#1 8	G#1 8	G1 8	F2 8
F2 8	F2 8	D2 2	- 8	G2 8	G2 8	F2 8	D#2 2	D2 8
G2 8	G2 8	F2 8	D#2 4	- 4	C2 4	- 4	G2 2

SYMPHONY NO. 40 THEME
By Wolfgang Amadeus Mozart

D#2 8	D2 8	D2 4	D#2 8	D2 8			TEMPO 225
D2 4	D#2 8	D2 8	D2 4	A#2 4	- 4	A#2 8	A2 8	G2 4
G2 8	F2 8	D#2 8	D#2 8	D2 8	C2 4	C2 4	- 4	D2 8
C2 8	C2 4	D2 8	C2 4	C2 8	D2 8	C2 4	C2 4	A2 4
- 4	A2 8	G2 8	F#2 4	F#2 8	D#2 8	D2 4	D2 8	C2 8
A#1 4	A#1 4

SYMPHONY NO. 94 ('SURPRISE')
By Joseph Haydn

C2 16	- 16	C2 16	- 16	E2 16			TEMPO 160
- 16	E2 16	- 16	G2 16	- 16	G2 16	- 16	E2 4	F2 16
- 16	F2 16	- 16	D2 16	- 16	D2 16	- 16	B1 16	- 16
B1 16	- 16	G1 4	C2 16	- 16	C2 16	- 16	E2 16	- 16
E2 16	- 16	G2 16	- 16	G2 16	- 16	E2 4	C3 16	- 16
C3 16	- 16	F#2 16	- 16	F#2 16	- 16	G2 8	- 8	G3 8

TOCCATA AND FUGUE
By Johann Sebastian Bach

A1 8	D2 8	E2 8	F2 8	D2 8			TEMPO 140
E2 8	F2 8	G2 8	E2 8	F2 8	G2 8	A2 8	F2 8	G2 8
A2 8	A#2 8	G2 8	A2 8	F2 8	G2 8	E2 8	F2 8	D2 8
E2 8	C#2 8	D2 8	A1 8	A#1 8	G1 8	A1 8	F1 8	G1 8
E1 8	F1 8	D1 8	G1 8	E1 8	F1 8	D1 8	E1 8	C#1 8
D1 8	- 8	A#1 8	- 8	A1 8	- 8	G1 8	- 8	A1 8

TRUMPET VOLUNTARY
By Jeremiah Clarke

G1 2	A1 32	B1 32	A1 32	B1 32			TEMPO 140
A1 32	B1 32	A1 4	G1 16	A1 16	B1 4.	C2 8	B1 4	A1 4
G1 4	A1 4	B1 4	A1 8	G1 8	A1 4	D1 4	D1 4	D1 4
G1 2	A1 32	B1 32	A1 32	B1 32	A1 32	B1 32	A1 4	G1 16
A1 16	B1 4.	C2 8	B1 4	A1 4	G1 8	A1 8	G1 8	A1 8
A1 32	B1 32	A1 32	B1 32	A1 32	B1 32	A1 4	G1 8	G1 2.

TROUT QUINTET
By Franz Schubert

TEMPO 140

TURKISH MARCH
By Wolfgang Amadeus Mozart

TEMPO 140

THE WELL-TEMPERED CLAVIER
(PRELUDE IN C MAJOR)
By Johann Sebastian Bach

E1 16	G1 16	C2 16	E2 16	G1 16	TEMPO 112
C2 16	E2 16	- 16	E1 16	G1 16	C2 16	E2 16	G1 16	C2 16
E2 16	- 16	D1 16	A1 16	D2 16	F2 16	A1 16	D2 16	F2 16
- 16	D1 16	A1 16	D2 16	F2 16	A1 16	D2 16	F2 16	- 16
D1 16	G1 16	D2 16	F2 16	G1 16	D2 16	F2 16	- 16	D1 16
G1 16	D2 16	F2 16	G2 16	D1 16	F2 16	- 16	E2 16	E2 4

VIOLIN SONATA IN E FLAT
By Wolfgang Amadeus Mozart

G1 8	A#1 8	A#1 16	- 16	D#2 16	TEMPO 125
- 16	D2 8	F2 8	G#2 4	G2 8	D#2 8
C2 8	F2 8	D#2 4	D2 8	- 8	G2 8
B1 8	C2 16	- 16	D#2 16	- 16	A1 8
C2 8	F2 4.	D#2 16	D2 16	C2 16	- 16
D2 16	- 16	A#1 4			

JAZZ & CLASSICAL